Study Guide to Accompany

THE HUMAN BODY IN HEALTH AND DISEASE

Prepared by
Linda Swisher, R.N., M.A.
Sarasota Vocational Technical Center
Sarasota, Florida

Mosby-Year Book, Inc.
St. Louis • Baltimore • Boston • Chicago • London • Philadelphia • Sidney • Toronto

Editor: Deborah Allen
Developmental Editor: Amy Winston
Production Editor: Donna Walls
Cover design: Gary Kaemmer

Printed in the United States of America

Mosby-Year Book, Inc.
11830 Westline Industrial Drive
St. Louis, MO 63146

ISBN 0-8016-6409-8

CONTENTS

PREFACE

TO THE INSTRUCTOR

This study guide is designed to help your students master basic anatomy and physiology. It works in two ways.

First, the section of the preface, titled "To the Student," contains detailed instructions on:

How to achieve good grades in anatomy and physiology
How to read the textbook
How to use the exercises in this study guide
How to use visual memory as a learning tool
How to use mnemonic devices as learning aids
How to prepare for an examination
How to take an examination
How to find out why questions were missed on an examination

Second, the study guide itself contains features that facilitate learning. These features include the following:

1. **LEARNING OBJECTIVES**, designed to break down the process of learning into small units. The questions in this study guide have been developed to help the student master the learning objectives identified at the beginning of each chapter in the text. The guide is also sequenced to correspond to key areas of each chapter. A variety of questions have been prepared to cover the material effectively and expose the student to multiple learning approaches.

2. **CROSSWORD PUZZLES**, to encourage the use of new vocabulary words and emphasize the proper spelling of these terms.

3. **OPTIONAL APPLICATION QUESTIONS**, particularly targeted for the health occupations student, but appropriate for any student of anatomy and physiology because they are based entirely on information contained within the chapter.

4. **DIAGRAMS**, with key features marked by numbers for identification. Students can easily check their work by comparing the diagram in the workbook with the equivalent figure in the text.

5. **PAGE NUMBER REFERENCES**, in the answer sections. Each answer is keyed to the appropriate text page. Additionally, questions are grouped into specific topics that correspond to the text. Each major topic of the study guide provides references to specific areas of the text, so that students having difficulty with a particular grouping of questions have a specific reference area to assist them with remedial work. This is of great assistance to both instructor and student, because remedial work is made easier and more effective when the area of weakness is identified accurately.

These features should make mastery of the material a rewarding experience for both instructor and student.

HOW TO ACHIEVE GOOD GRADES IN ANATOMY AND PHYSIOLOGY

This study guide is designed to help you help yourself to be successful in learning anatomy and physiology. Before you begin using the study guide, read the following suggestions. Students who understand effective study techniques and who have good study habits are successful students.

HOW TO READ THE TEXTBOOK

Keep up with the reading assignments. Read the textbook assignment prior to instructor covering the material in lecture. If you have failed to read the assignment beforehand, you will not grasp what the instructor is talking about in lecture. When you read, do the following:

1. As you finish reading a sentence, ask yourself if you understand it. If you do not, put a question mark in the margin by that sentence. If the instructor does not clear up the problem in lecture, ask him or her to explain it to you.

2. Do the learning objectives in the text. A learning objective is a specific task that you are expected to be able to do after you have read a chapter. It sets specific goals for the student and breaks down learning into small steps. It emphasizes the key points that the author is making in the chapter.

3. Underline and make notes in the margin to highlight key ideas, to mark something you need to reinforce at a later time, or to indicate things that you do not understand.

4. If you come to a word you do not understand, look it up in a dictionary. Write the word on one side of an index card and its definition on the other side. Carry these cards with you, and when you have a spare minute, use them in the way that you used flash cards to learn multiplication tables. If you do not know how to spell or pronounce a word, you will have a hard time remembering it.

5. Carefully study each diagram and illustration as you read. Many students ignore these aids. The author included them for a reason: to help students understand the material.

6. Summarize what you read. After finishing a paragraph, try to restate the main ideas. Do this again when you finish the chapter. Identify and review in your mind the main concepts of the chapter. Check to see if you are correct. In short, be an *active* reader. Do not just stare at a page or read it superficially.

Finally, attack each unit of learning with a positive mental attitude. Motivation and perseverance are prime factors in achieving successful grades. The combination of your instructor, the text, the study guide, and your dedicated work will lead to success for you in anatomy and physiology.

HOW TO USE THE EXERCISES IN THIS STUDY GUIDE

After you have read a chapter and learned all the new words, begin working with the study guide. Read the overview of the chapter, which summarizes the main points.

Familiarize yourself with the Topics for Review section, which repeats the learning objectives outlined in the text. Complete the questions and diagrams in the study guide. The questions are sequenced to follow the chapter outline and headings and are divided into small sections to facilitate learning. A variety of questions is offered throughout the study guide to help you cover the material effectively. The following examples are among the exercises that have been included to assist you.

Multiple Choice Questions

Multiple choice questions will have only one correct answer out of several possibilities for you to select. There are two types of multiple choice questions that you may not be acquainted with:

1. "None of the above is correct" questions. These questions test your ability to recall rather than recognize the correct answer. You would select the "none of the above" choice only if all the other choices in that particular question were incorrect.

2. Sequence questions. These questions test your ability to arrange a list of structures in the correct order. In this type of question you are asked to determine the sequence of the structures given in the various choices, and then you are to select the structure listed that would be third in that sequence, as in this example.

> Which one of the following structures would be the third through which food would pass?
>
> a. Stomach   d. Esophagus
> b. Mouth   e. Anus
> c. Large intestine

The correct answer would be a.

Matching Questions

Matching questions ask the student to select the correct answer from a list of terms and to write the answer in the space provided.

True or False

True or false questions ask you to write T in the answer space, if you agree with that statement. If you disagree with the statement, you will circle the incorrect word(s) and write the correct word(s) in the answer space.

Identify the Incorrect Term

In questions that ask you to identify the incorrect term, three words are given that relate to each other in structure or function, and one more word is included that has no relationship, or has an opposing relationship to the other three terms. You are to circle the term that does not relate to the other terms. An example might be: iris, cornea, stapes, retina. You would circle the word *stapes* because all other terms refer to the eye.

Fill in the Blanks

Fill-in-the-blank questions ask you to recall missing word(s) and insert it or them into the answer blank(s). These questions may be sentences or paragraphs.

Application

Application questions ask you to make judgments about a situation based on the information in the chapter. These questions may ask you how you would respond to a situation or to suggest a possible diagnosis for a set of symptoms.

Charts

Several charts have been included that correspond to figures in the text. Areas have been omitted so that you can fill them in and test your recall of these important areas.

Identification

The study guide includes word find puzzles that allow you to identify key terms in the chapter in an interesting and challenging way.

Crossword Puzzles

Vocabulary words from the New Words section at the end of each chapter of the text have been developed into crossword puzzles. This not only encourages recall, but also proper spelling. Occasionally, an exercise uses scrambled words to encourage recall and spelling.

Labeling Exercises

Labeling exercises present diagrams with parts that are not identified. For each of these diagrams you are to print the name of each numbered part on the appropriately numbered line. You may choose to further distinguish the structures by coloring them with a variety of colors. After you have written down the names of all the structures to be identified, check your answers. When it comes time to review before an examination you can place a sheet of paper over the answers that you have already written on the lines. This procedure will allow you to test yourself without peeking at the answers.

After completing the exercises in the study guide, check your answers. If they are not correct, refer to the page listed with the answer, and review it for further clarification. If you still do not understand the question or the answer, ask your instructor for further explanation.

If you have difficulty with several questions from one section, refer to the pages given at the end of the section. After reviewing the section, try to answer the questions again. If you are still having difficulty, talk to your instructor.

HOW TO USE VISUAL MEMORY

Visual memory is another important tool in learning. If I asked you to picture an elephant in your mind, with all its external parts labeled, you could do that easily. Visual memory is a powerful key to learning. Whenever possible, try to build a memory picture. Remember, a picture is worth a thousand words.

Visual memory works especially well with the sequencing of items, such as circulatory pathways and the passage of air or food. Students who try to learn sequencing by memorizing a list of words do poorly on examinations. If they forget one word in the sequence, then they will forget all the words after the forgotten one as well. However, with a memory picture you can pick out the important features.

HOW TO USE MNEMONIC DEVICES

Mnemonic devices are little jingles you memorize to help you remember things. If you make up your own, they will stick with you longer. Here are three examples of such devices:

"On Old Olympus' towering tops a Finn and German viewed some hops." This one is used to remember the cranial nerves; each word begins with the same letter as does the name of one of the nerves.

"C. Hopkins CaFe where they serve Mg NaCl." This mnemonic reminds you of the chemical symbols for the biologically important electrolytes.

"Roy G. Biv." This mnemonic helps you remember the colors of the visible light spectrum.

HOW TO PREPARE FOR AN EXAMINATION

Prepare far in advance for an examination. Actually, your preparation for an examination should begin on the first day of class. Keeping up with your assignments daily makes the final preparation for an examination much easier. You should begin your final preparation at least three nights before the test. Last-minute studying usually means poor results and limited retention.

1. Make sure that you understand and can answer all of the learning objectives for the chapter on which you are being tested.

2. Review the appropriate questions in this study guide. Reviewing is something that you should do after every class and at the end of every study session. It is important to keep going over the material until you have a thorough understanding of the chapter and rapid recall of its contents. If review becomes a daily habit, studying for the actual examination will not be difficult. Go through each question and write down an answer. Do the same with the labeling of each structure on the appropriate diagrams. If you have already done this as part of your daily review, cover the answers with a piece of paper and quiz yourself again.

3. Check the answers that you have written down against the correct answers in the back of the study guide. Go back and study the areas in the text that refer to questions that you missed and then try to answer those questions again. If you still cannot answer a question or label a structure correctly, ask your instructor for help.

4. Ask yourself as you read a chapter what questions you would ask if you were writing a test on that unit. You will most likely ask yourself many of the questions that will show up on your examinations.

5. Get a good night's sleep before the test. Staying up late and upsetting your biorhythms will only make you less efficient during the test.

HOW TO TAKE AN EXAMINATION

The Day of the Test

1. Get up early enough to avoid rushing. Eat appropriately; your body needs fuel, but a heavy meal just before a test is not a good idea.

2. Keep calm. Briefly look over your notes. If you have prepared for the test properly, there will be no need for last-minute cramming.

3. Make certain that you have everything you need for the test — pens, pencils, test sheets, and so forth.

4. Allow enough time to get to the examination site. Missing your bus, getting stuck in traffic, or being unable to find a parking space will not put you in a good frame of mind to do well on the examination.

During the Examination

1. Pay careful attention to the instructions for the test.

2. Note any corrections.

3. Budget your time so that you will be able to finish the test.

4. Ask the instructor for clarification if you do not understand a question or an instruction.

5. Concentrate on your own test paper and do not allow yourself to be distracted by others in the room.

Hints for Taking a Multiple Choice Test

1. Read each question carefully. Pay attention to each word.

2. Cross out obviously wrong choices and think about those that are left.

3. Go through the test once, quickly answering the questions you are sure of. Then go back over the test and answer the rest of the questions.

4. Fill in the answer spaces completely and make your marks heavy. Erase completely if you make a mistake.

5. If you must guess, stick with your first hunch. Most often, students will change right answers to wrong ones.

6. If you will not be penalized for guessing, do not leave any blanks.

Hints for Taking an Essay Test

1. Budget time for each question.

2. Write legibly and try to spell words correctly.

3. Be concise, complete, and specific. Do not be repetitious or long-winded.

4. Organize your answer in an outline which helps not only the student but also the person who grades the test.

5. Answer each question as thoroughly as you can, but leave some room for possible additions.

Hints for Taking a Laboratory Practical Examination

Students have a hard time with this kind of test. Visual memory is very important here. To put it simply, you must be able to identify every structure you have studied. If you are unable to identify a structure, then you will be unable to answer any questions about that structure.

Possible questions that could appear on an examination of this type might include:

1. Identification of a structure, organ, feature.

2. Function of a structure, organ, feature.

3. Sequence questions for air flow, passage of food, urine, and so forth.

4. Disease questions (e.g., if an organ fails, what disease will result?).

HOW TO FIND OUT WHY QUESTIONS WERE MISSED ON AN EXAMINATION

After the Examination

Go over your test after it has been scored to see what you missed and why you missed it. You can pick up important clues that will help you on future examinations. Ask yourself these questions:

1. Did I miss questions because I did not read them carefully?

2. Did I miss questions because I had gaps in my knowledge?

3. Did I miss questions because I could not determine scientific words?

4. Did I miss questions because I did not have good visual memory of things?

Be sure to go back and learn the things you did not know. Chances are these topics will come up on the final examination.

Your grades in other classes as well will improve greatly when you apply these study methods. Learning should be fun. With these helpful hints and this study guide you should be able to achieve the grades you desire. Good luck!

ACKNOWLEDGEMENTS

I wish to express my appreciation to the staff of Mosby-Year Book, especially Deborah Allen, Laura Edwards and Amy Winston for opening this door. My continued admiration and thanks to Gary Thibodeau and Kevin Patton for an outstanding text. Your time and dedication to science education will, hopefully, create a better quality of health care for the future.

Special thanks to Alice Tatakis for her perseverance and enthusiasm while transposing the written word to typed script.

A. Christine Payne and her computer combined efforts to produce crossword puzzles and word finds for the units. Her creativity added the variety necessary to stimulate the learning process.

To my daughter, Amanda, my students, colleagues and friends, my thanks for your assistance and support.

Finally, to the designer of the human body this book is dedicated. What a miraculous creation!

Linda Swisher, RN, M.A.

CHAPTER 1

An Introduction to the Structure and Function of the Body

A command of terminology is necessary for a student to be successful in any area of science. This chapter defines the terminology and concepts that are basic to the field of anatomy and physiology. Building a firm foundation in these language skills will assist you with all future chapters.

The study of anatomy and physiology involves the structure and function of an organism and the relationship of its parts. It begins with a basic organization of the body into different structural levels. Beginning with the smallest level (the cell) and progressing to the largest, most complex level (the system), this chapter familiarizes you with the terminology and the levels of organization needed to facilitate the study of the body as a part or as a whole.

It is also important to be able to identify and to describe specific body areas or regions as we progress in this field. The anatomical position is used as a reference position when dissecting the body into planes, regions, or cavities. The terminology defined in this chapter allows you to describe the areas efficiently and accurately.

Finally, the process of homeostasis is reviewed. This state of relative constancy in the chemical composition of body fluids is necessary for good health. In fact, the very survival of the body depends on the successful maintenance of homeostasis.

TOPICS FOR REVIEW

Before progressing to Chapter 2, you should have an understanding of the structural levels of organization; the planes, regions, and cavities of the body; the terminology used to describe these areas, and the concept of homeostasis as it relates to the survival of the species.

STRUCTURAL LEVELS OF ORGANIZATION

Match the term on the left with the proper selection on the right.

Group A

_____ 1. Organism	a.	Many similar cells that act together to perform a common function
_____ 2. Cells	b.	The most complex units that make up the body
_____ 3. Tissue	c.	A group of several different kinds of tissues arranged to perform a
_____ 4. Organ		special function
_____ 5. Systems	d.	Denotes a living thing
	e.	The smallest "living" units of structure and function in the body

Group B

_____ 6. Dorsal	a.	Chest cavity
_____ 7. Ventral	b.	Area below the hipbone
_____ 8. Thoracic	c.	Toward the back
_____ 9. Pelvic	d.	Separates the thoracic cavity from the abdominal cavity
_____ 10. Diaphragm	e.	Toward the belly

▶ If you have had difficulty with this section, review pages 1-6. ◀

SOME WORDS USED IN DESCRIBING BODY STRUCTURES, PLANES, OR SECTIONS

Fill in the crossword puzzle.

11. Upper or above
12. Lower or below
13. Horizontal plane
14. Front (abdominal side)
15. Toward the side of the body
16. Toward the midline of the body
17. Farthest from the point of origin of a body point

Circle the correct answer.

18. The bladder is (superior or inferior) to the transverse colon.

19. The nose is located on the (anterior or posterior) surface of the body.

20. The lungs lie (medial or lateral) to the heart.

21. The elbow lies (proximal or distal) to the forearm.

22. The skin is (superficial or deep) to the muscles below it.

23. A midsagittal plane divides the body into (equal or unequal) parts.

24. A frontal plane divides the body into (anterior and posterior or superior and inferior) sections.

25. A transverse plane divides the body into (right and left or upper and lower) sections.

2

26. The liver lies in the (right upper quadrant or right lower quadrant).

27. In the anatomical position the palms of the hands are pointing (forward or backward).

> ▸ If you have had difficulty with this section, review pages 5-9. ◂

BODY REGIONS

Circle the one that does <u>not</u> belong.

28. Axial	Head	Trunk	Extremities
29. Axillary	Cephalic	Brachial	Antecubital
30. Frontal	Orbital	Plantar	Nasal
31. Erect	Anatomical position	Feet forward	Eyes closed
32. Inguinal	Navel	Plantar	Mammary
33. Carpal	Femoral	Plantar	Pedal
34. Thoracic	Dorsal	Gluteal	Popliteal

> ▸ If you have had difficulty with this section, review pages 5-9. ◂

If the following statement is true, insert "T" in the answer blank. If the statement is false, circle the incorrect word(s) and insert the correct word(s) in the answer blank.

_____ 35. The term autopsy comes from the Greek words *auto* (self) and *opsis* (view).
_____ 36. Autopsies are usually performed in four stages.
_____ 37. In the first stage of an autopsy, the exterior of the body is examined for abnormalities such as wounds or scars.
_____ 38. The face arms, and legs are usually dissected during the second stage of an autopsy.
_____ 39. Microscopic examination of tissues occurs during all stages of an autopsy.
_____ 40. Tests to analyze the chemical content of body fluids or to determine the presence of infectious organisms may also be performed during an autopsy.

> ▸ If you have had difficulty with this section, review page 12. ◂

SOME BASIC FACTS ABOUT BODY FUNCTIONS

Fill in the blanks.

41. _____ depends on the body's ability to maintain or restore homeostasis.

42. "Homeostasis" is the term used to describe the relative constancy of the body's

_____.

43. In the absence of homeostasis, body CO2 levels would _____ _____.

3

44. Changes and functions that occur during the early years are called _____.

45. Changes and functions that occur after young adulthood are called _____.

46. Homeostatic control mechanisms are categorized as either _____ or _____ feedback loops.

47. Negative feedback loops are _____ mechanisms.

48. Positive feedback control loops are _____.

▸ If you have had difficulty with this section, review pages 12-13. ◂

APPLYING WHAT YOU KNOW

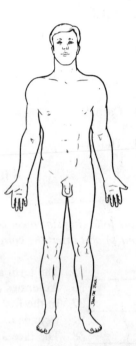

49. Mrs. Fagan has had an appendectomy. The nurse is preparing to change the dressing. She knows that the appendix is located in the right iliac inguinal region, the distal portion extending at an angle into the hypogastric region. Place an X on the diagram where the nurse will place the dressing.

50. Mrs. Suchman noticed a lump in her breast. Dr. Reeder noted on her chart that a small mass was located in the left breast medial to the nipple. Place an X where Mrs. Suchman's lump would be located.

51. Jeff was injured in a bicycle accident. X-ray films revealed that he had a fracture of the right patella. A cast was applied beginning at the distal femoral region and extending to the pedal region. Place an X where Jeff's cast begins and ends.

DID YOU KNOW?

Many animals produce tears but only humans weep as a result of emotional stress.

DORSAL AND VENTRAL BODY CAVITIES

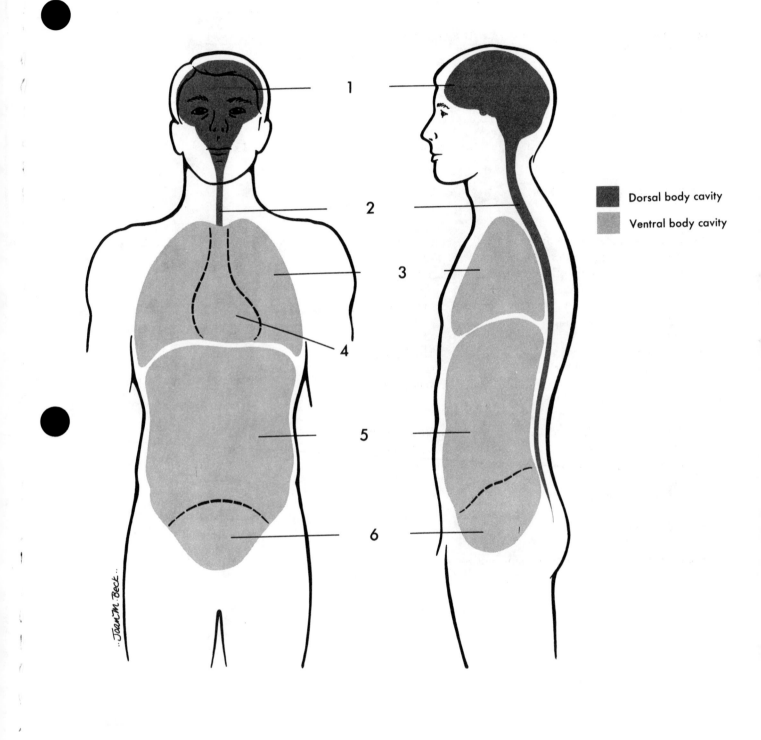

Dorsal body cavity

Ventral body cavity

1. _____   4. _____

2. _____   5. _____

3. _____   6. _____

DIRECTIONS AND PLANES OF THE BODY

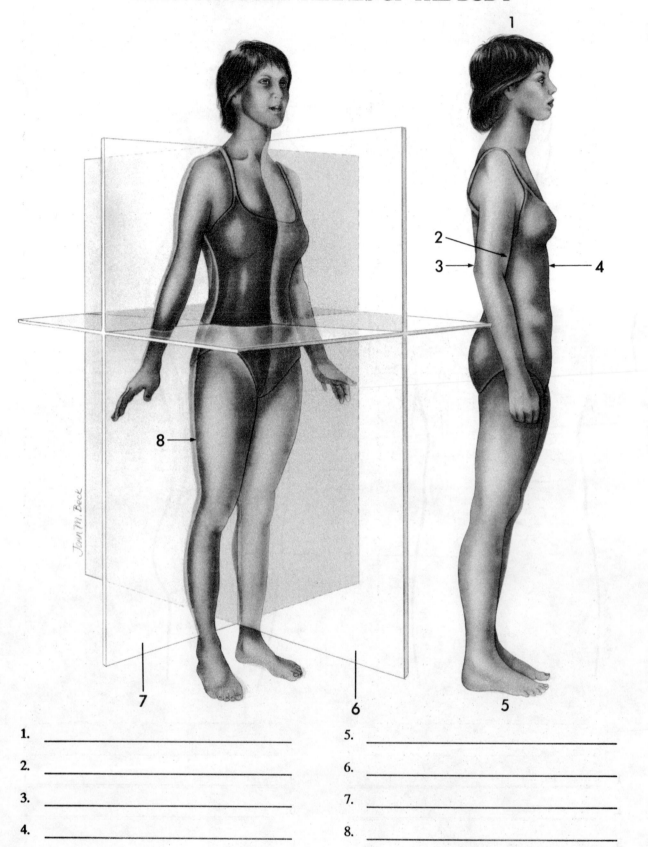

1. _____ 5. _____

2. _____ 6. _____

3. _____ 7. _____

4. _____ 8. _____

6

REGIONS OF THE ABDOMEN

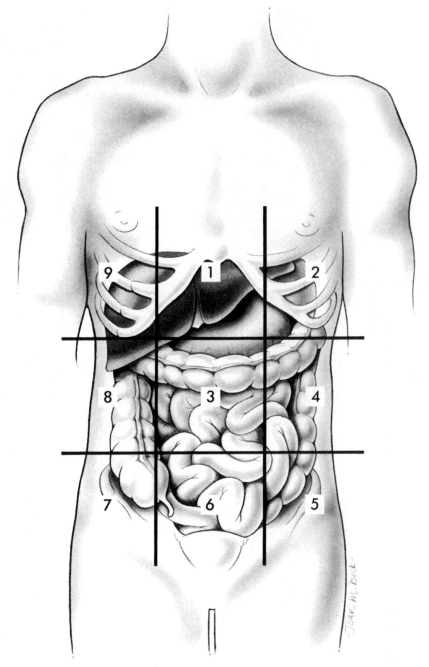

1. _____

2. _____

3. _____

4. _____

5. _____

6. _____

7. _____

8. _____

9. _____

CHAPTER 2

Cells and Tissues

Cells are the smallest structural units of living things. Therefore, because we are living, we are made up of a mass of cells. Human cells can be viewed only microscopically; they vary in shape and size. The three main parts of a cell are the cytoplasmic membrane, the cytoplasm, and the nucleus. As you review the chapter on cells, you will be amazed at the cells' resemblance to the body as a whole. You will identify miniature circulatory systems, reproductive systems, digestive systems, power plants much like the muscular system, and many others that will aid in your understanding of these systems in future chapters.

Cells, just like humans, depend on water, food, gases, elimination of wastes, and numerous other substances. The movement of these substances in and out of the cells is accomplished by two primary methods: passive transport processes and active transport processes. In passive transport processes no cellular energy is required to effect movement through the cell membrane. However, in active transport cellular energy is required to effect movement through the cell membrane.

Cell reproduction completes the study of cells. A basic explanation of DNA, "the hereditary molecule," gives us a proper respect for the capability of the cell to transmit physical and mental traits from generation to generation. Reproduction of the cell, mitosis, is a complex process requiring several stages. These stages are outlined and diagramed in the text to facilitate learning.

This chapter concludes with the discussion of tissues. The four main types of tissues, epithelial, connective, muscle, and nervous, are reviewed. The characteristics, location, and function of these tissues are necessary to complete your understanding of the next structural level of organization.

TOPICS FOR REVIEW

Before progressing to Chapter 3, you should have an understanding of the structure and function of the smallest living unit in the body—the cell. Your review should also include the methods by which substances are moved through the cell membrane and the stages necessary for the cell to reproduce. The study of this chapter is completed with an understanding of tonicity and body tissues and the function they perform in the body.

CELLS

Match the term on the left with the proper selection on the right.

Group A

_____ 1. Cytoplasm	a.	Component of plasma membrane
_____ 2. Plasma membrane	b.	Controls reproduction of the cell
_____ 3. Cholesterol	c.	"Living matter"
_____ 4. Nucleus	d.	Paired organelles
_____ 5. Centrioles	e.	Surrounds cells

Group B

____ 6. Ribosomes	a.	"Power plants"
____ 7. Endoplasmic	b.	"Digestive bags"
reticulum	c.	"Carbohydrate producing and packaging factory"
____ 8. Mitochondria	d.	"Protein factories"
____ 9. Lysosomes	e.	Miniature "circulatory system"
____ 10. Golgi apparatus		

Fill in the blanks.

11. A system where measurement of length is based on the meter is known as the _____.

12. A procedure performed prior to transplanting an organ from one individual to another is _____.

13. Fine, hairlike extensions found on the exposed or free surfaces of some cells are called _____.

14. This organelle is distinguished by the fact that it has two types. It may be either smooth or rough _____.

15. _____ are usually attached to rough endoplasmic reticulum and produce enzymes and other protein compounds.

16. The _____ provide energy-releasing chemical reactions that go on continuously.

17. The organelles that can digest and destroy microbes that invade the cell are called _____.

18. Mucus is an example of a product manufactured by the _____.

19. These rod-shaped structures, _____, play an important role during cell division.

20. _____ are threadlike structures made up of proteins and DNA.

21. When the immune systems mounts a significant attack against the donated tissue, a _____ occurs.

22. The test used to test for the presence of antibodies produced in response to the HIV virus is known as _____.

▸ If you have had difficulty with this section, review pages 19-26. ◂

MOVEMENT OF SUBSTANCES THROUGH CELL MEMBRANES

Circle the correct choice.

23. The energy required for active transport processes is obtained from:

    a. ATP   c. Diffusion
    b. DNA   d. Osmosis

24. An example of a passive transport process is:

a. Permease system
b. Phagocytosis

c. Pinocytosis
d. Diffusion

25. Movement of substances from a region of high concentration to a region of low concentration is known as:

a. Active transport
b. Passive transport

c. Cellular energy
d. Concentration gradient

26. Osmosis is the _____ of water across a selectively permeable membrane.

a. Filtration
b. Equilibrium

c. Active transport
d. Diffusion

27. _____ involves the movement of solutes across a selectively permeable membrane by the process of diffusion.

a. Osmosis
b. Filtration

c. Dialysis
d. Phagocytosis

28. A specialized example of diffusion is:

a. Osmosis
b. Permease system

c. Filtration
d. All of the above

29. This movement always occurs down a hydrostatic pressure gradient.

a. Osmosis
b. Filtration

c. Dialysis
d. Facilitated diffusion

30. The uphill movement of a substance through a living cell membrane is:

a. Osmosis
b. Diffusion

c. Active transport process
d. Passive transport process

31. The sodium pump is an example of this type of movement.

a. Osmosis
b. Pinocytosis

c. Permease system
d. Diffusion

32. An example of a cell that uses phagocytosis is the:

a. White blood cell
b. Red blood cell

c. Muscle cell
d. Bone cell

33. A saline solution that contains a higher concentration of salt than living red blood cells would be:

a. Hypotonic
b. Hypertonic

c. Isotonic
d. Homeostatic

34. A red blood cell becomes engorged with water and will eventually lyse, releasing hemoglobin into the solution. This solution is _____ to the red blood cell.

    a. Hypotonic   c. Isotonic
    b. Hypertonic   d. Homeostatic

► If you have had difficulty with this section, review pages 26-30. ◄

CELL REPRODUCTION

Circle the one that does <u>not</u> belong.

35. DNA	Adenine	Uracil	Thymine
36. Complementary base pairing	Guanine	RNA	Cytosine
37. Anaphase	Specific sequence	Gene	Base pairs
38. RNA	Ribose	Thymine	Uracil
39. Double helix	Mitosis	DNA	Replication
40. Cleavage furrow	Anaphase	Prophase	2 daughter cells
41. "Resting"	Prophase	Interphase	DNA replication
42. Identical	2 nuclei	Telophase	Metaphase
43. Metaphase	Prophase	Telophase	Gene

TISSUES

44. *Fill in the missing area.*

TISSUE	LOCATION	FUNCTION
Epithelial		
1. Simple squamous	1a. Alveoli of lungs	1a.
	1b. Lining of blood and lymphatic vessels	1b.
2. Stratified squamous	2a.	2a. Protection
	2b.	2b. Protection
3. Simple columnar	3.	3. Protection, secretion, absorption

4.	4. Urinary bladder	4. Protection
5. Pseudostratified	5.	5. Protection

Connective

1. Areolar	1.	1. Connection
2.	2. Under skin	2. Protection; insulation
3. Dense fibrous	3. Tendons; ligaments; fascia, scar tissue	3.
4. Bone	4.	4. Support, protection
5. Cartilage	5.	5. Firm but flexible support
6. Blood	6. Blood vessels	6.
7.	7. Red bone marrow	7. Blood cell formation

Muscle

1. Skeletal (striated voluntary)	1.	1. Movement of bones
2.	2. Wall of heart	2. Contraction of heart
3. Smooth	3.	3. Movement of substances along ducts; change in diameter of pupils and shape of lens; "gooseflesh"

Nervous

1.	1.	1. Irritability, conduction

▸ If you have had difficulty with this section, review Table 2-4 and pages 36-47. ◂

APPLYING WHAT YOU KNOW

45. Mr. Fee's boat had capsized, and he was stranded on a deserted shoreline for 2 days without food or water. When found, he had swallowed a great deal of seawater. He was taken to the emergency room in a state of dehydration. In the space to the right, draw the appearance of the red blood cells as they would appear to the laboratory technician.

46. The nurse was instructed to dissolve a pill in a small amount of liquid medication. As she dropped the capsule into the liquid, she was interrupted by the telephone. On her return to the medication cart, she found the medication completely dissolved and apparently scattered evenly throughout the liquid. This phenomenon did not surprise her since she was aware from her knowledge of cell transport that _____ had created this distribution.

47. Mrs. Henion has emphysema and has been admitted to the hospital unit with oxygen per nasal cannula. Emphysema destroys the tiny air sacs in the lungs, reducing the diffusion of oxygen into the blood. These tiny air sacs, alveoli, are formed by what type of tissue?

48. Merrily was 5'4" and weighed 115 lbs. She appeared very healthy and fit, yet her doctor advised her that she was "overfat." What might be the explanation for this assessment?

DID YOU KNOW?

The largest single cell in the human body is the female sex cell, the ovum. The smallest single cell in the human body is the male sex cell, the sperm.

CELLS AND TISSUES

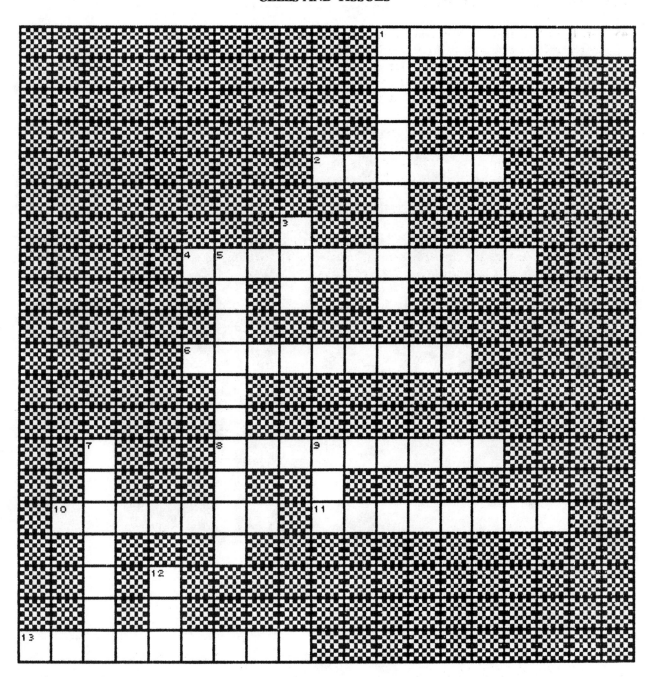

<u>Across</u>

1. Specialized example of diffusion
2. Nerve cell
4. Cartilage cell
6. Last stage of mitosis
8. Cell organ
10. Reproduction process of most cells
11. First stage of mitosis
13. Shriveling of cell due to water withdrawal

<u>Down</u>

1. Occurs when substances scatter themselves evenly throughout an available space
3. Ribonucleic acid (abbreviation)
5. Having an osmotic pressure greater than that of the solution of which it is compared
7. Fat
9. Energy source for active transport
12. Chemical "blueprint" of the body (abbreviation)

CELL STRUCTURE

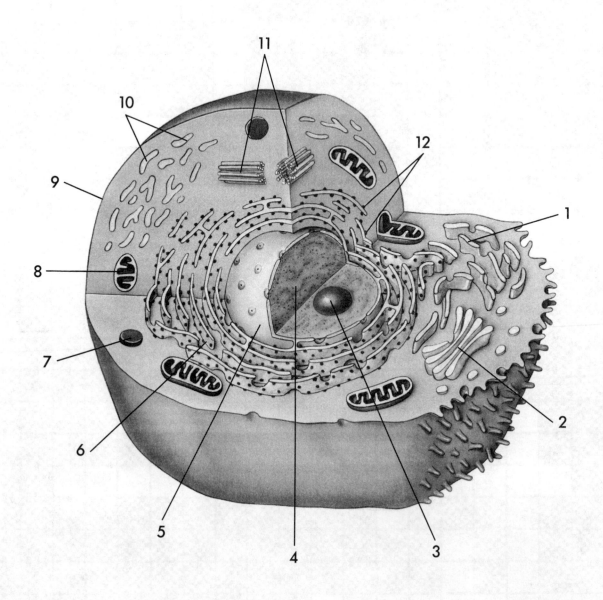

1. _____

2. _____

3. _____

4. _____

5. _____

6. _____

7. _____

8. _____

9. _____

10. _____

11. _____

12. _____

MITOSIS

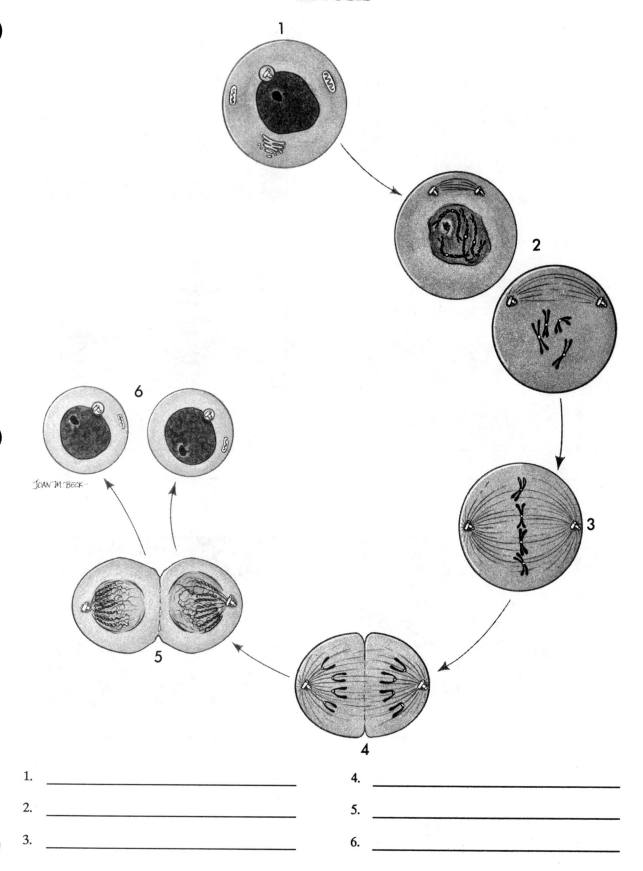

1. _____   4. _____

2. _____   5. _____

3. _____   6. _____

TISSUES

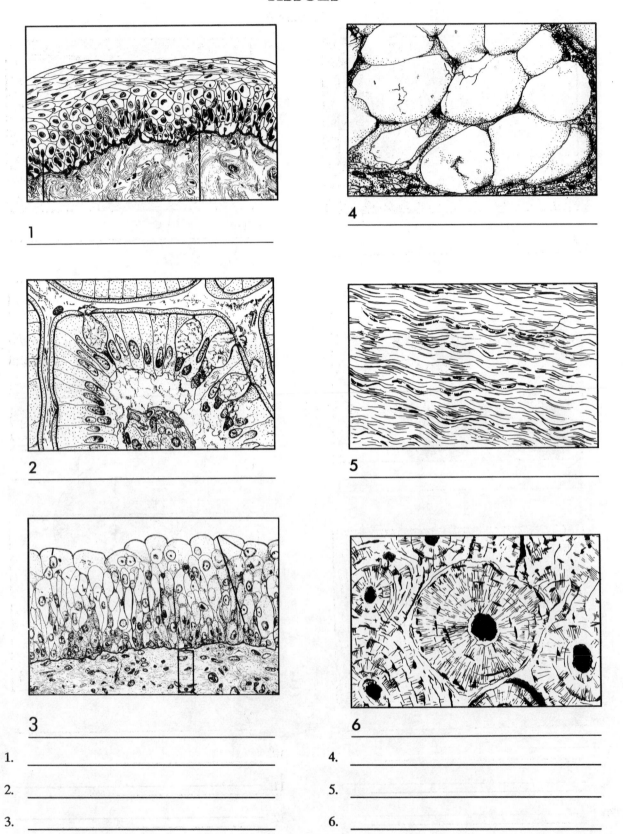

1 _____

4 _____

2 _____

5 _____

3 _____

1. _____

2. _____

3. _____

6 _____

4. _____

5. _____

6. _____

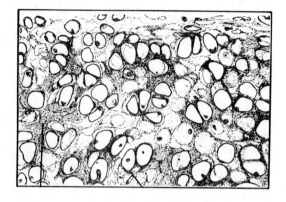

7 _____

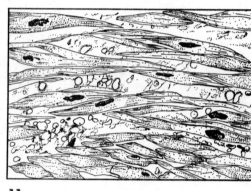

10 _____

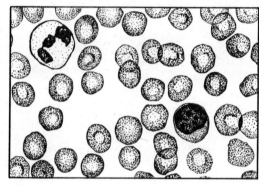

8 _____

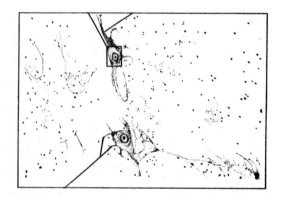

11 _____

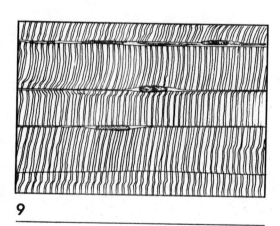

9 _____

12 _____

7. _____

8. _____

9. _____

10. _____

11. _____

12. _____

CHAPTER 3

Organ Systems of the Body

A smooth-running automobile is the result of many systems working harmoniously. The engine, the fuel system, the exhaust system, the brake system, and the cooling system are but a few of the many complex structural units that the automobile as a whole relies on to keep it functioning smoothly. So it is with the human body. We, too, depend on the successful performance of many individual systems working together to create a healthy human being.

When you have completed your review of the 11 major organ systems and the organs that make up these systems, you will find your understanding of the performance of the body as a whole much more meaningful.

TOPICS FOR REVIEW

Before progressing to Chapter 4, you should have an understanding of the 11 major organ systems and be able to identify the organs that are included in each system. Your review should also include current approaches to organ replacement.

ORGAN SYSTEMS OF THE BODY

Match the term on the left with the proper selection on the right.

Group A

_____	1.	Integumentary	a.	Hair
_____	2.	Skeletal	b.	Spinal cord
_____	3.	Muscular	c.	Hormones
_____	4.	Nervous	d.	Tendons
_____	5.	Endocrine	e.	Joints

Group B

_____	6.	Circulatory	a.	Pharynx
_____	7.	Lymphatic	b.	Ureters
_____	8.	Urinary	c.	Larynx
_____	9.	Digestive	d.	Genitalia
_____	10.	Respiratory	e.	Spleen
_____	11.	Reproductive	f.	Capillaries

Circle the one that does __not__ belong.

12. Pharynx	Trachea	Mouth	Alveoli
13. Uterus	Rectum	Gonads	Prostate
14. Veins	Arteries	Heart	Pancreas
15. Pineal	Bladder	Ureters	Urethra
16. Tendon	Smooth	Joints	Voluntary
17. Pituitary	Brain	Spinal cord	Nerves
18. Cartilage	Joints	Ligaments	Tendons
19. Hormones	Pituitary	Pancreas	Appendix
20. Thymus	Nails	Hair	Oil glands
21. Esophagus	Pharynx	Mouth	Trachea
22. Thymus	Spleen	Tonsils	Liver

Fill in the missing area.

SYSTEM	ORGANS	FUNCTIONS
23. Integumentary	Skin, nails, hair, sense receptors, sweat glands, oil glands	
24. Skeletal		Support, movement, storage of minerals, blood formation
25. Muscular	Muscles	
26.	Brain, spinal cord, nerves	Communication, integration, control, recognition of sensory stimuli
27. Endocrine		Secretion of hormones; communication, integration, control
28. Circulatory	Heart, blood vessels	
29. Lymphatic		Transportation, immune system
30.	Kidneys, ureters, bladder, urethra	Elimination of wastes, electrolyte balance, acid-base balance, water balance
31. Digestive		Digestion of food, absorption of nutrients
32.	Nose, pharynx, larynx, trachea, bronchi, lungs	Exchange of gases in the lungs
33. Reproductive		Survival of species; production of sex cells, fertilization, development, birth; nourishment of offspring; production of hormones

▸ If you have had difficulty with this section, review pages 56-66 and the chapter summary on pages 70-71. ◂

ORGAN REPLACEMENT

Fill in the blanks.

34.   An organ not required for life to continue is a _____.

35.   Many people suffering from deafness have had their hearing partially restored by "artificial ears" called _____ _____.

36.   One of the earliest devices to augment vital functions was the "artificial kidney" or _____ _____.

37.   An example of an artificial heart is the _____.

38.   One approach that offers the hope of a permanent solution to loss of vital organ function is _____ _____.

39.   After cancerous breasts are removed, "new" breasts can be formed from skin and muscle tissue using a method known as _____ _____.

40.   The advantage to using a patient's own tissues in organ replacement is that the possibility of _____ is eliminated.

▸ If you have had difficulty with this section, review pages 66-69. ◂

Unscramble the words.

41. RTAHE

42. IEPLNA

43. EENVR

44. SUHESOPGA

Take the circled letters, unscramble them, and fill in the statement.

The more thoroughly you review this chapter the less

45. ☐☐☐☐☐☐☐ **you will be during your test**

APPLYING WHAT YOU KNOW

46. Myrna was 15 years old and had not yet started menstruating. Her family physician decided to consult two other physicians, each of whom specialized in a different system. Specialists in the areas of _____ and _____ were consulted.

47. Brian was admitted to the hospital with second-degree and third-degree burns over 50% of his body. He was placed in isolation, so when Jenny went to visit him, she was required to wear a hospital gown and mask. Why was Brian placed in isolation? Why was Jenny required to wear special attire?

DID YOU KNOW?

Muscles comprise 40% of your body weight. Your skeleton, however, only accounts for 18% of your body weight.

ORGAN SYSTEMS

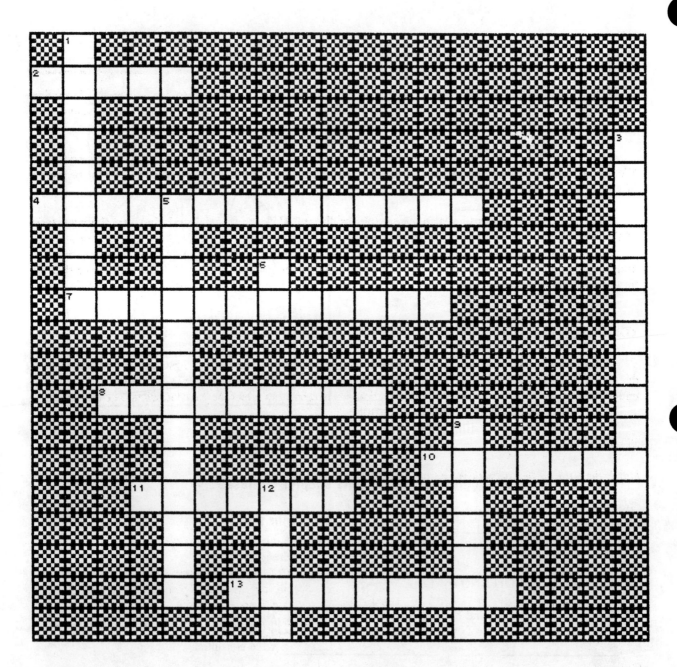

ACROSS

2. Undigested residue of digestion
4. Heart and blood vessels
7. Inflammation of the appendix
8. Subdivision of circulatory system
10. Testes and ovaries
11. Agent that causes change in the activity of a structure
13. System of hormones

DOWN

1. Vulva, penis, and scrotum
3. Specialized signal of nervous system (two words)
5. Skin
6. Gastrointestinal tract (abbrev.)
9. Chemical secretion of endocrine system
12. Waste product of kidneys

CHAPTER 4

Mechanisms of Disease

One of our foremost concerns is health. We are fascinated and constantly confronted with information regarding what is necessary to be in good health, what is required for proper maintenance of the body, and what behaviors are responsible for disease.

Organisms play an important role in health. They are microscopic structures that are present everywhere. We need organisms in the preparation of some foods in industry and agriculture, in connection with the problems of shelter or clothing and in combating disease.

However, some organisms are also responsible for disease. They attack and disturb the normal homeostasis of the body. Many varieties of organisms exist. They are often classified by shape, size, function, or staining properties. To prevent disease we must prevent pathogenic or disease-producing organisms from entering the body. This is not an easy task because we are surrounded by pathogenic organisms. It is important then that we understand the transmission and control of these organisms to fully comprehend the mechanisms of disease.

TOPICS FOR REVIEW

Before progressing to Chapter 5 you should familiarize yourself with disease terminology and patterns of disease. You should continue your review by studying pathophysiology and pathogenic organisms. Finally, an understanding of tumors, cancer, and inflammation are necessary to conclude your knowledge of this chapter.

STUDYING DISEASE

Match the term on the left with the proper selection on the right.

Group A

_____	1.	Pathology
_____	2.	Signs
_____	3.	Symptoms
_____	4.	Syndrome
_____	5.	Etiology

a. Subjective abnormalities
b. Study of disease
c. Collection of different signs and symptoms that present a clear picture of a pathological condition
d. Study of factors involved in causing a disease
e. Objective abnormalities

Group B

_____	6.	Latent
_____	7.	Convalescence
_____	8.	Pandemics
_____	9.	Endemic
_____	10.	Pathogenesis

a. Recovery
b. Disease native to a local region
c. "Hidden" stage
d. Affects large geographic regions
e. Actual pattern of a disease's development

▸ If you have had difficulty with this section, review page 74. ◂

PATHOPHYSIOLOGY

Fill in the blanks.

11. _____ is the organized study of the underlying physiological processes associated with disease.

12. Many diseases are best understood as disturbances of _____.

13. Altered or _____ genes can cause abnormal proteins to be made.

14. An organisms that lives in or on another organisms to obtain its nutrients is called a _____.

15. Abnormal tissue growths may also be referred to as _____.

16. Autoimmunity literally means _____ _____.

17. Genetic factors, age, lifestyle, stress, environmental factors, and preexisting conditions are

    _____ _____ that may be responsible for predisposing a person to disease.

18. The _____ _____ _____ _____ continuously tracks the incidence and spread of disease in this country and worldwide.

19. Conditions caused by psychological factors are sometimes called _____ disorders.

20. A primary condition can put a person at risk for developing a _____ condition.

▶ If you have difficulty with this section, review pages 75-77. ◀

PATHOGENIC ORGANISMS

Circle the best answer.

21. The smallest of all pathogens, microscopic nonliving particles are called:

    a. Bacteria
    b. Fungi
    c. Viruses
    d. Protozoa

22. A tiny, primitive cell without a nucleus is called a:

    a. Bacterium
    b. Fungus
    c. Virus
    d. Protozoa

23. An example of a viral disease is:

    a. Diarrhea
    b. Mononucleosis
    c. Syphilis
    d. Toxic shock syndrome

24. Bacteria that require oxygen for metabolism are classified as:

    a.   Gram positive   c.   Aerobic
    b.   Gram negative   d.   Anaerobic

25. Bacilli are shaped like:

    a.   Spheres   c.   Squares
    b.   Curves   d.   Rods

26. Without chlorophyll _____ cannot produce their own food, so they must consume or parasitize other organisms.

    a.   Bacteria   c.   Viruses
    b.   Fungi   d.   Protozoa

27. Protozoa include:

    a.   Amoebas   c.   Ciliates
    b.   Flagellates   d.   All of the above

28. Pathogenic animals include the following:

    a.   Nematodes   c.   Arthropods
    B.   Platyhelminths   d.   All of the above

29. The key to preventing diseases caused by pathogenic organisms is to:

    a.   Have an annual physical
    b.   Stop them from entering the body
    c.   Isolate yourself from all disease carrying individuals
    d.   None of the above

30. The destruction of all living organisms is known as:

    a.   Disinfection   c.   Sterilization
    b.   Antisepsis   d.   Isolation

31. Ways in which pathogens can spread include:

    a.   Person to person contact   d.   Transmission by vector
    b.   Environmental contact   e.   All of the above
    c.   Opportunistic invasion

32. Compounds produced by certain living organisms that kill or inhibit pathogens are:

    a.   Antiseptics   c.   Disinfectants
    b.   Antibiotics   d.   Sterilizers

▸ If you have had difficulty wit this section, review pages 78-87. ◂

TUMORS AND CANCER

Circle the correct answer.

33. Benign tumors usually grow (slowly or quickly).

34. Malignant tumors (are or are not) encapsulated.

35. An example of a benign tumor that arises from epithelial tissue is (papilloma or lipoma).

36. A general term for malignant tumors that arise from connective tissues is (melanoma or sarcoma).

37. Abnormal, undifferentiated tumor cells are often produced by a process called (hyperplasia or anaplasia).

38. A cancer specialist is an (osteologist or oncologist).

39. The Papanicolaou test is a (biopsy or MRI).

40. (Staging or Grading) involves classifying a tumor based on its size and the extent of its spread.

41. Cachexia involves a loss of (appetite or hair).

▶ If you have had difficulty with this section, review pages 87-92. ◀

WARNING SIGNS OF CANCER

List the seven warning signs of cancer.

42. _____

43. _____

44. _____

45. _____

46. _____

47. _____

48. _____

▶ If you have had difficulty with this section, review page 90. ◀

INFLAMMATION

*If the statement is true, write **T** in the answer blank. If the statement is false, correct the statement by circling the incorrect term and inserting the correct term in the answer blank.*

_____ 49. As tissue cells are damaged, they release inflammation mediators such as histamines, prostaglandins, and kinins.

_____ 50. Inflammatory exudate is quickly removed by lymphatic vessels and is carried to lymph nodes, which act as filters.

_____ 51. Inflammation mediators can also act as signals that attract red blood cells to the injury site.
_____ 52. The movement of white blood cells in response to chemical attractants is called chemotaxis.
_____ 53. When new cells are similar to those that they replace, the process is known as replacement.
_____ 54. Fevers usually subside after the irritant has been eliminated.
_____ 55. The fever response in children and in the elderly often differs from that in the normal adult.

APPLYING WHAT YOU KNOW

56. Mrs. Calhoun was examined by her doctor and was diagnosed as having a rhinovirus. Does Mrs. Calhoun have need for concern? Why or why not?

57. Julius was 2 years old and was experiencing rectal itching and insomnia. The pediatrician told Julius' mother that he suspected a nematode. What is the common term for the specific nematode that might cause these symptoms?

58. Shirley was cleaning her house and wanted to use the most appropriate and effective aseptic method to prevent the spread of germs. What would you suggest?

MAJOR GROUPS OF PATHOGENIC BACTERIA

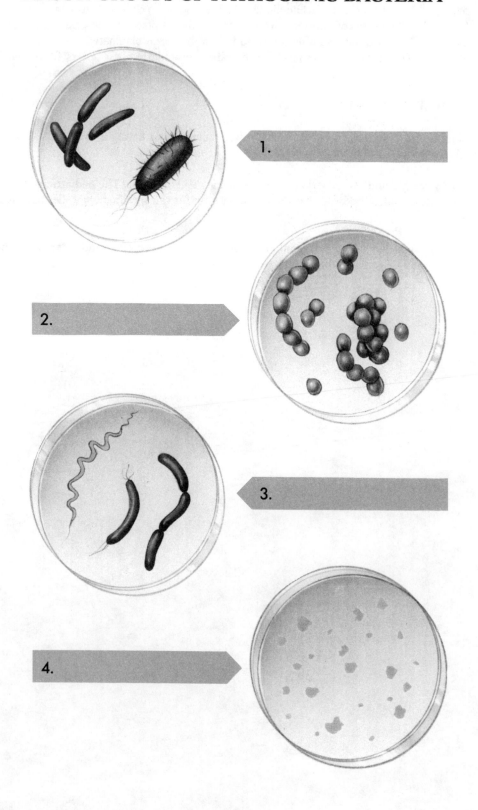

1.

2.

3.

4.

1.

2.

MAJOR GROUPS OF PATHOGENIC PROTOZOA

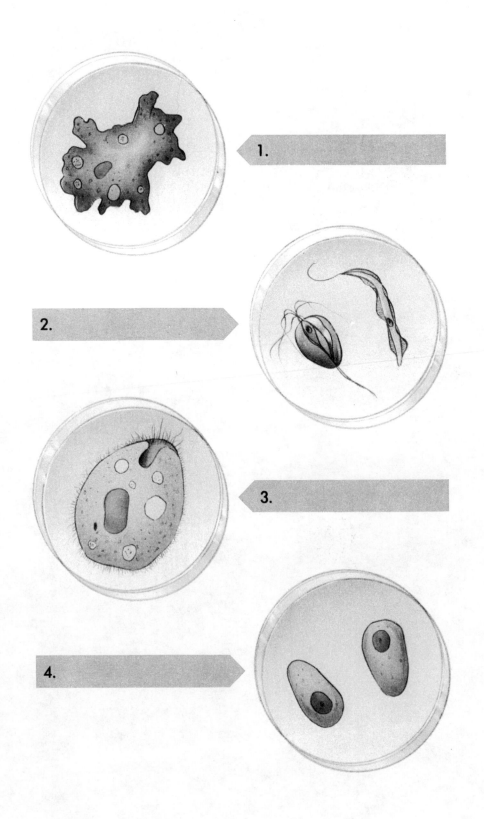

EXAMPLES OF PATHOGENIC ANIMALS

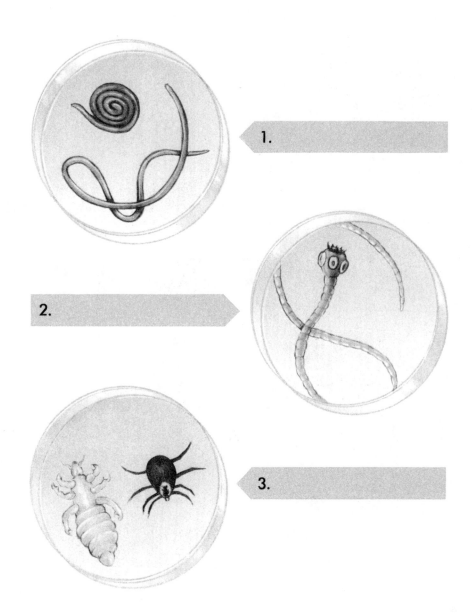

CHAPTER 5

The Integumentary System and Body Membranes

More of our time, attention, and money are spent on this system than any other one. Every time we look into a mirror we become aware of the integumentary system, as we observe our skin, hair, nails, and the appendages that give luster and comfort to this system. The discussion of the skin begins with the structure and function of the two primary layers called the epidermis and dermis. It continues with an examination of the appendages of the skin, which include the hair, receptors, nails, sebaceous glands, and sudoriferous glands. Your study of skin concludes with a review of one of the most serious and frequent threats to the skin — burns. An understanding of the integumentary system provides you with an appreciation of the danger that severe burns could pose to this system.

Membranes are thin sheetlike structures that cover, protect, anchor, or lubricate body surfaces, cavities, or organs. The two major categories are epithelial and connective. Each type is located in specific areas of the body and is vulnerable to specific disease conditions. Knowledge of the location and function of these membranes prepares you for the study of their relationship to other systems and the body as a whole.

TOPICS FOR REVIEW

Before progressing to Chapter 6, you should have an understanding of the skin, its appendages, major skin disorders, and infections. Your review should include the classification of burns and the method used to estimate the percentage of body surface area affected by burns. A knowledge of the types of body membranes, their location, and their function is necessary to complete your study of this chapter.

CLASSIFICATION OF BODY MEMBRANES

Select the best answer.

(a) Cutaneous   (b) Serous   (c) Mucous   (d) Synovial

_____ 1. Pleura
_____ 2. Lines joint spaces
_____ 3. Respiratory tract
_____ 4. Skin
_____ 5. Peritoneum
_____ 6. Contains no epithelium
_____ 7. Urinary tract
_____ 8. Lines body surfaces that open directly to the exterior

▶ If you have had difficulty with this section, review pages 102-104. ◀

THE SKIN

Match the term on the left with the proper selection on the right.

Group A

_____ 9. Integumentary system	a. Outermost layer of skin
_____ 10. Epidermis	b. Deeper of the two layers of skin
_____ 11. Dermis	c. Allows for rapid absorption of injected material
_____ 12. Subcutaneous	d. The skin is the primary organ
_____ 13. Cutaneous membrane	e. Composed of dermis and epidermis

Group B

_____ 14. Keratin	a. Protective protein
_____ 15. Melanin	b. Blue-gray color of skin resulting from a decrease in oxygen
_____ 16. Stratum corneum	c. Rows of peglike projections
_____ 17. Dermal papillae	d. Brown pigment
_____ 18. Cyanosis	e. Outer layer of epidermis

Select the best answer.

(a) Epidermis   (b) Dermis

_____ 19. Tightly packed epithelial cells
_____ 20. Nerves
_____ 21. Fingerprints
_____ 22. Blisters
_____ 23. Keratin
_____ 24. Connective tissue
_____ 25. Follicle
_____ 26. Sebaceous gland
_____ 27. Sweat gland
_____ 28. More cellular than other layer

▶ If you have had difficulty with this section, review pages 102-112. ◀

Fill in the blanks.

29. The three most important functions of the skin are _____, _____, and

_____.

30. _____ prevents the sun's ultraviolet rays from penetrating the interior of the body.

31. The hair of a newborn infant is called _____.

32. Hair growth begins from a small cap-shaped cluster of cells called the _____.

33. Hair loss of any kind is called _____.

34. The _____ muscle produces "goose pimples."

35. Meissner's corpuscle is generally located rather close to the skin surface and is capable of detecting sensations of _____.

36. The most numerous, important, and widespread sweat glands in the body are the _____ sweat glands.

37. The _____ sweat glands are found primarily in the axilla and in the pigmented skin areas around the genitals.

38. _____ has been described as "nature's skin cream."

Circle the correct answer.

39. A first-degree burn (will or will not) blister.

40. A second-degree burn (will or will not) scar.

41. A third-degree burn (will or will not) have pain immediately.

42. According to the "rule of nines" the body is divided into (9 or 11) areas of 9%.

43. Destruction of the subcutaneous layer occurs in (second- or third-) degree burns.

▶ If you have had difficulty with this section, review pages 108-113. ◀

DISORDERS OF THE SKIN

44. Any disorders of the skin may be called:

    a.   Dermatitis
    b.   Dermatosis

    c. Dermatotomy
    d. None of the above

45. Any measurable variation from the normal structure of a tissue is known as a/an:

    a.   Lesion
    b.   Burn

    c. Blister
    d. Erythema

46. An example of a papule is a:

    a.   Scratch
    b.   Bedsore

    c. Freckle
    d. Wart

47. An example of a skin disorder that may produce fissures is:

    a.   Acne
    b.   A bedsore

    c. Psoriasis
    d. Athlete's foot

48. The skin is the _____ line of defense against microbes that invade the body's internal environment.

    a.   First
    b.   Second

    c. Third
    d. Fourth

49. Tinea is a fungal infection and may appear as:

    a.   Ringworm
    b.   Jock itch

    c. Athlete's foot
    d. All of the above

50. Furuncles are local staphylococci infections and are also known as:

    a.   Scabies
    b.   Warts

    c. Boils
    d. Impetigo

51. The most common type of skin cancer is:

    a.   Squamous cell
    b.   Basal cell

    c. Melanoma
    d. Kaposi's sarcoma

▶ If you had difficulty with this section, review pages 112-119. ◀

Unscramble the words.

52. PIDEEMIRS

53. REKTAIN

54. AHIR

55. UGONAL

56. DRTONIDEHYA

Take the circled letters, unscramble them, and
fill in the statement.
What Amanda's mother gave her after every date.

57.

APPLYING WHAT YOU KNOW

58. Mr. Ziven was admitted to the hospital with second-degree and third-degree burns. Both arms, the anterior trunk, the right anterior leg, and the genital region were affected by the burns. The doctor quickly estimated that _____% of Mr. Ziven's body had been burned.

59. Mrs. James complained to her doctor that she had severe pain in her chest and feared that she was having a heart attack. An ECG revealed nothing unusual, but Mrs. James insisted that every time she took a breath she experienced pain. What might be the cause of Mrs. James' pain?

60. Mrs. Collins was born with a rare condition known as xeroderma pigmentosum. What activity should she avoid?

DID YOU KNOW?

Because the dead cells of the epidermis are constantly being worn and washed away, we get a new outer skin layer every 27 days.

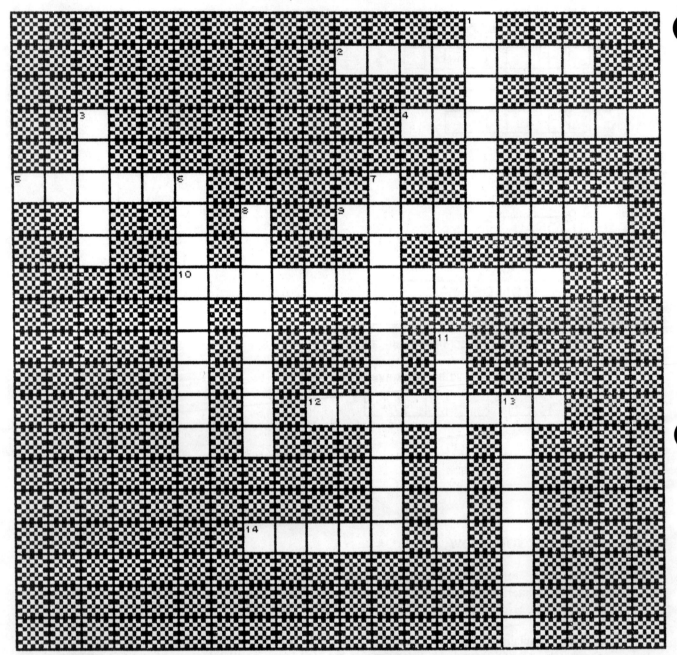

ACROSS

2. Covers the surface of organs found in serous body cavities
4. Bluish gray color of skin due to decreased 02
5. Deeper of the two primary skin layers
9. Skin
10. "Goose pimples" (two words)
12. Inflammation of the serous membrane that lines the chest and covers the lungs
14. A thick secretion that keeps mucous membranes soft and moist

DOWN

1. Brown pigment
3. Cushionlike sacs found between moving body parts
6. Oil gland
7. Sweat gland
8. Forms the lining of serous body cavities
11. Tough waterproof substance that protects body from excessive fluid loss
13. Membrane that lines joint spaces

LONGITUDINAL SECTION OF THE SKIN

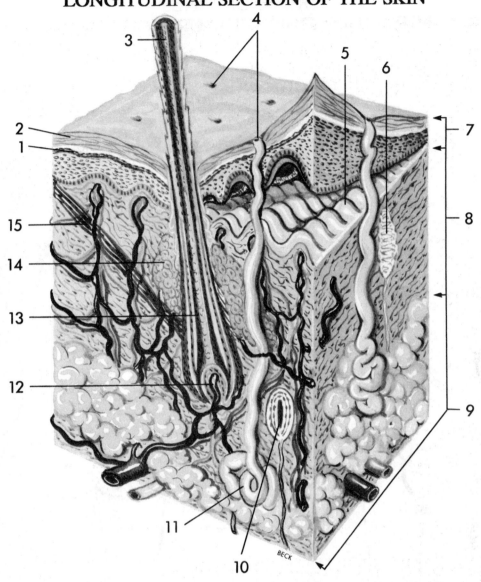

BECK

1. _____
2. _____
3. _____
4. _____
5. _____
6. _____
7. _____
8. _____

9. _____
10. _____
11. _____
12. _____
13. _____
14. _____
15. _____

43

"RULE OF NINES"
FOR ESTIMATING SKIN SURFACE BURNED

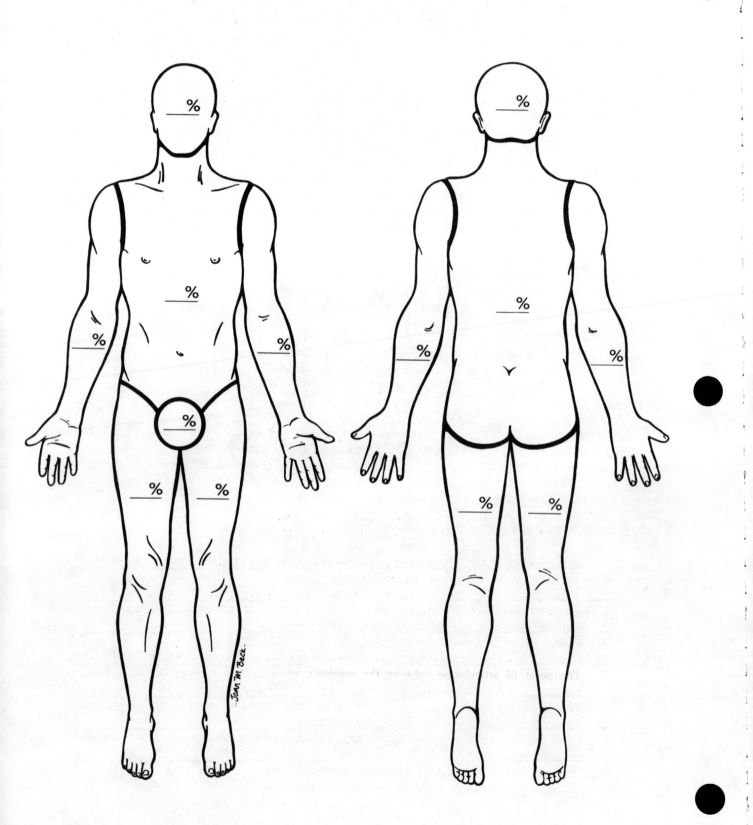

CHAPTER 6

The Skeletal System

How strange we would look without the skeleton, because it is the skeleton that provides us with the rigid, supportive framework that gives shape to our bodies. But this is just the beginning, since it also protects the organs beneath it, maintains homeostasis of blood calcium, produces blood cells, and assists the muscular system in providing movement for us.

After reviewing the microscopic structure of bone and cartilage, you will understand how skeletal tissues are formed, their differences, and their importance in the human body. Your microscopic investigation will make the study of this system easier as you logically progress from this view to macroscopic bone formation and growth and visualize the structure of long bones.

The skeleton is divided into two main divisions: the axial skeleton and the appendicular skeleton. All of the 206 bones of the human body may be classified into one of these two areas. And, although we can divide them neatly by this system, we are still aware that subtle differences exist between a man's and a woman's skeleton. These structural differences provide us with insight to the differences in function between men and women.

Finally, three types of joints exist in the body. They are synarthrosis, amphiarthrosis, and diarthrosis. It is important to have a knowledge of these joints to understand how movement is facilitated by articulations.

TOPICS FOR REVIEW

Before progressing to Chapter 7, you should familiarize yourself with the functions of the skeletal system, the structure and function of bone and cartilage, bone formation and growth, and the types of joints found in the body. Additionally, your understanding of the skeletal system should include identification of the two major subdivisions of the skeleton, the bones found in each area, and any differences that exist between a man's and a woman's skeleton. Your study should conclude with a review of the major skeletal disorders.

BONE FORMATION AND GROWTH

If the statement is true, write T in the answer blank. If the statement is false, correct the statement by circling the incorrect term and inserting the correct term in the answer blank.

_____ 1. When the skeleton forms in a baby before birth, it consists of cartilage and fibrous structures.

_____ 2. The diaphyses are the ends of the bone.

_____ 3. Bone-forming cells are known as osteoclasts.

_____ 4. It is the combined action of osteoblasts and osteoclasts that sculpts bones into their adult shapes.

_____ 5. The point of articulation between the epiphysis and diaphysis of a *growing* long bone is susceptible to injury if overstressed.

_____ 6. The epiphyseal plate can be seen in both external and cutaway views of an adult long bone.

_____ 7. The shaft of a long bone is known as the articulation.

_____ 8. Cartilage in the newborn becomes bone when it is replaced with calcified bone matrix deposited by osteoblasts.

_____ 9. When epiphyseal cartilage becomes bone, growth begins.

_____ 10. The epiphyseal cartilage is visible, if present, on x-ray films.

▸ If you have had difficulty with this section, review pages 128-129. ◂

MICROSCOPIC STRUCTURE OF BONE AND CARTILAGE

Match the term on the left with the proper selection on the right.

Group A

_____ 11. Trabeculae
_____ 12. Compact
_____ 13. Spongy
_____ 14. Periosteum
_____ 15. Cartilage

a. Outer covering of bone
b. Dense bone tissue
c. Fibers embedded in a firm gel
d. Needlelike threads of spongy bone
e. Ends of long bones

Group B

_____ 16. Osteocytes
_____ 17. Canaliculi
_____ 18. Lamellae
_____ 19. Chondrocytes
_____ 20. Haversian system

a. Connect lacunae
b. Cartilage cells
c. Structural unit of compact bone
d. Bone cells
e. Ring of bone

▸ If you have had difficulty with this section, review pages 128-131. ◂

TYPES OF BONES
STRUCTURE OF LONG BONES
FUNCTIONS

Fill in the blanks.

21. There are _____ types of bones.

22. The _____ _____ is the hollow area inside the diaphysis of a bone.

23. A thin layer of cartilage covering each epiphysis is the _____.

24. The _____ lines the medullary cavity of long bones.

25. _____ is used to describe the process of blood cell formation.

Circle the correct choice.

26. Which one of the following is *not* a part of the axial skeleton?

a. Scapula
b. Cranial bones
c. Vertebra

d. Ribs
e. Sternum

27. Which one of the following is *not* a cranial bone?

    a. Frontal
    b. Parietal
    c. Occipital

    d. Lacrimal
    e. Sphenoid

28. Which of the following is *not* correct?

    a. A baby is born with a straight spine.
    b. In the adult the sacral and thoracic curves are convex.
    c. The normal curves of the adult spine provide greater strength than a straight spine.
    d. A curved structure has more strength than a straight one of the same size and materials.

29. True ribs:

    a. Attach to the cartilage of other ribs
    b. Do not attach to the sternum
    c. Attach directly to the sternum without cartilage
    d. Attach directly to the sternum by means of cartilage

30. The bone that runs along the thumb side of your forearm is the:

    a. Humerus
    b. Ulna

    c. Radius
    d. Tibia

31. The shinbone is also known as the:

    a. Fibula
    b. Femur

    c. Tibia
    d. Ulna

32. The bones in the palm of the hand are called:

    a. Metatarsals
    b. Tarsals

    c. Carpals
    d. Metacarpals

33. Which one of the following is *not* a bone of the upper extremity?

    a. Radius
    b. Clavicle

    c. Humerus
    d. Ilium

34. The heel bone is known as the:

    a. Calcaneus
    b. Talus

    c. Metatarsal
    d. Phalanges

35. The mastoid process is part of which bone?

    a. Parietal
    b. Temporal

    c. Occipital
    d. Frontal

36. When a baby learns to walk, which area of the spine becomes concave?

    a. Lumbar
    b. Thoracic

    c. Cervical
    d. Coccyx

37. Which bone is the "funny" bone?

a. Radius   c. Humerus
b. Ulna   d. Carpal

38. There are how many pair of true ribs?

a. 14   c. 5
b. 7   d. 3

39. The 27 bones in the wrist and the hand allow for more:

a. Strength   c. Protection
b. Dexterity   d. Red blood cell products

40. The longest bone in the body is the:

a. Tibia   c. Femur
b. Fibula   d. Humerus

41. Distally, the _____ articulates with the patella.

a. Femur   c. Tibia
b. Fibula   d. Humerus

42. These bones form the cheek bones:

a. Mandible   c. Maxillary
b. Palatine   d. Zygomatic

43. In a child, there are five of these bones. In an adult, they are fused into one:

a. Pelvic   c. Sacrum
b. Lumbar vertebrae   d. Carpals

44. The spinal cord enters the cranium through a large hole (foramen magnum) in this bone:

a. Temporal   c. Occipital
b. Parietal   d. Sphenoid

Circle the one that does <u>not</u> belong.

45. Cervical	Thoracic	Os coxae	Coccyx
46. Pelvic girdle	Ankle	Wrist	Axial
47. Frontal	Occipital	Maxillary	Sphenoid
48. Scapula	Pectoral girdle	Ribs	Clavicle
49. Malleus	Vomer	Incus	Stapes
50. Ulna	Ilium	Ischium	Pubis

51. Carpal	Phalanges	Metacarpal	Ethmoid
Ethmoid	Parietal	Occipital	Nasal
53. Anvil	Atlas	Axis	Cervical

► If you have had difficulty with this section, review pages 132-149. ◄

DIFFERENCES BETWEEN A MAN'S AND A WOMAN'S SKELETON

Choose the right answer.

(a) Male   (b) Female

_____54. Funnel-shaped pelvis
_____55. Broader-shaped pelvis
_____56. Osteoporosis occurs more frequently
_____57. Larger
_____58. Wider pelvic brim

► If you have had difficulty with this section, review pages 150-155. ◄

BONE MARKINGS

m the choices given, match the bone with its identification marking. Bones may be used more than once.

a. Mastoid
b. Pterygoid process
c. Foramen magnum
d. Sella turcica
e. Mental foramen
f. Conchae
g. Xiphoid process
h. Glenoid cavity
i. Olecranon process
j. Ischium

k. Acetabulum
l. Symphysis pubis
m. Ilium
n. Greater trochanter
o. Medial malleolus
p. Calcaneus
q. Acromion process
r. Frontal sinuses
s. Condyloid process
t. Tibial tuberosity

_____59. Occipital
_____60. Sternum
_____61. Os coxae
_____62. Femur
_____63. Ulna
_____64. Temporal
_____65. Tarsals
_____66. Sphenoid
_____67. Ethmoid
_____68. Scapula
_____69. Tibia
_____70. Frontal
_____71. Mandible

49

▶ If you have had difficulty with this section, review pages 136-149. ◀

JOINTS (ARTICULATIONS)

Circle the correct answer.

72. Freely movable joints are (amphiarthroses or diarthroses).

73. The sutures in the skull are (synarthrotic or amphiarthrotic) joints.

74. All (diarthrotic or amphiarthrotic) joints have a joint capsule, a joint cavity, and a layer of cartilage over the ends of the two joining bones.

75. (Ligaments or tendons) grow out of periosteum and attach two bones together.

76. The (articular cartilage or epiphyseal cartilage) absorbs jolts.

77. Gliding joints are the (least movable or most movable) of the diarthrotic joints.

78. The knee is the (largest or smallest) joint.

79. Hinge joints allow motion in (2 or 4) directions.

80. The saddle joint at the base of each of our thumbs allows for greater (strength or mobility).

81. When you rotate your head, you are using a (gliding or pivot) joint.

▶ If you have had difficulty with this section, review pages 147-154. ◀

Fill in the blanks.

82. _____ is an imaging technique that allows a physician to examine the internal structure of a joint without the use of extensive surgery.

83. One of the most common skeletal tumors and one of the most rapidly fatal is _____.

84. A metabolic disorder involving mineral loss in bones is _____.

85. A metabolic disorder which is often asymptomatic and affects older adults is _____.

86. The general name for bacterial infections of bone and marrow tissue is _____.

87. Closed fractures, also known as _____ _____, do not pierce the skin.

88. _____ _____ are breaks that produce many fragments.

89. The most common noninflammatory joint disease is _____ or _____

   _____ _____.

90. Three major types of arthritis are _____, _____, and

   _____.

91. One form of infectious arthritis, _____ _____, was identified in 1975 in Connecticut and has since spread across the continent.

▸ If you have had difficulty with this section, review pages 155-159. ◂

Unscramble the bones.

92. ETVERRBAE

93. BPSUI

94. SCALUPA

95. IMDBALNE

96. APNHGAELS

Take the circled letters, unscramble them, and fill in the statement.

What the fat lady wore to the ball.

97.

APPLYING WHAT YOU KNOW

98. Mrs. Perine had advanced cancer of the bone. As the disease progressed, Mrs. Perine required several blood transfusions throughout her therapy. She asked the doctor one day to explain the necessity for the transfusions. What explanation might the doctor give to Mrs. Perine?

99. Dr. Kennedy, an orthopedic surgeon, called the admissions office of the hospital and advised that he would be admitting a patient in the next hour with an epiphyseal fracture. Without any other information, the patient is assigned to the pediatric ward. What prompted this assignment?

100. Mrs. Van Skiver, age 60, noticed when she went in for her physical examination that she was a half inch shorter than she was on her last visit. Dr. Veazey suggested she begin a regimen of dietary supplements of calcium, vitamin D, and a prescription for sex hormone therapy. What bone disease did Dr. Veazey suspect?

DID YOU KNOW?

The bones of the hands and feet make up more than half of the total 206 bones of the body.

SKELETAL SYSTEM

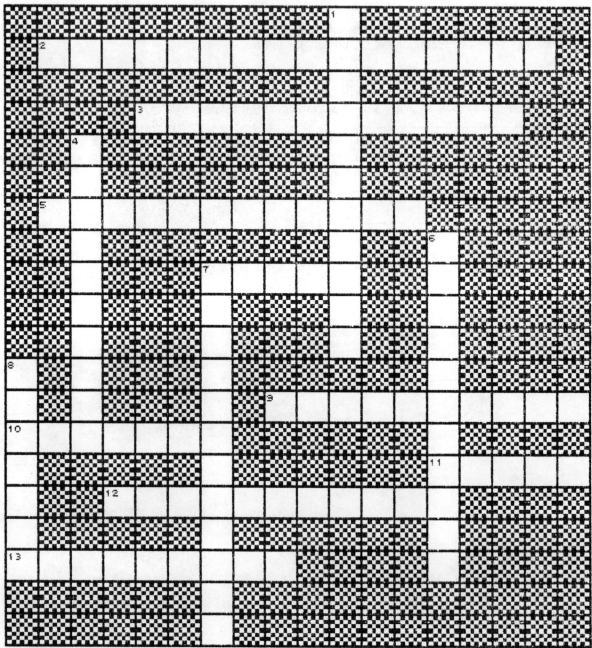

ACROSS

2. Lines joint capsule
3. Cartilage cells
5. Joint
7. Space inside cranial bone
9. Bone cells
10. Type of bone
11. Division of skeleton
12. Freely movable joints
13. Ends of long bones

DOWN

1. Process of blood cell formation
4. Covers long bone except at its joint surfaces
6. Bone absorbing cells
7. Suture joints
8. Spaces in bones where osteocytes are found

LONGITUDINAL SECTION OF LONG BONE

1. _____

2. _____

3. _____

4. _____

5. _____

6. _____

7. _____

8. _____

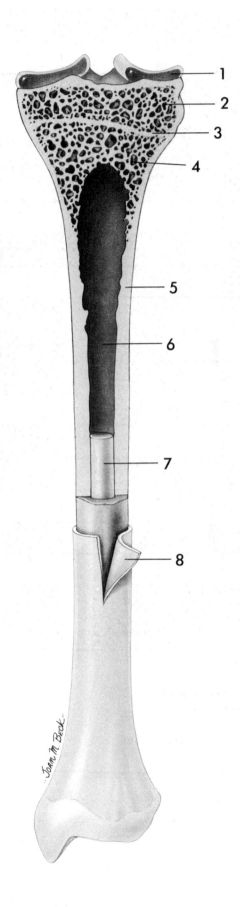

ANTERIOR VIEW OF SKELETON

1. _____
2. _____
3. _____
4. _____
5. _____
6. _____
7. _____
8. _____
9. _____
10. _____
11. _____
12. _____
13. _____
14. _____
15. _____
16. _____
17. _____
18. _____
19. _____
20. _____
21. _____
22. _____
23. _____
24. _____
25. _____
26. _____
27. _____
28. _____
29. _____
30. _____

56

POSTERIOR VIEW OF SKELETON

1. _____
2. _____
3. _____
4. _____
5. _____
6. _____
7. _____
8. _____
9. _____
10. _____
11. _____
12. _____
13. _____
14. _____

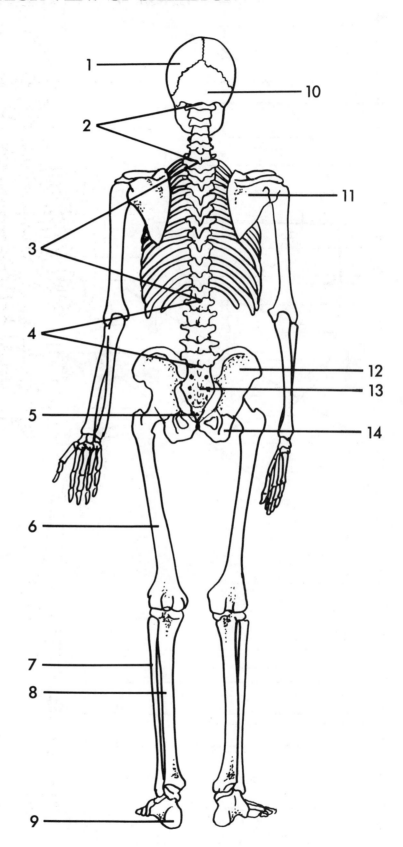

SKULL VIEWED FROM THE RIGHT SIDE

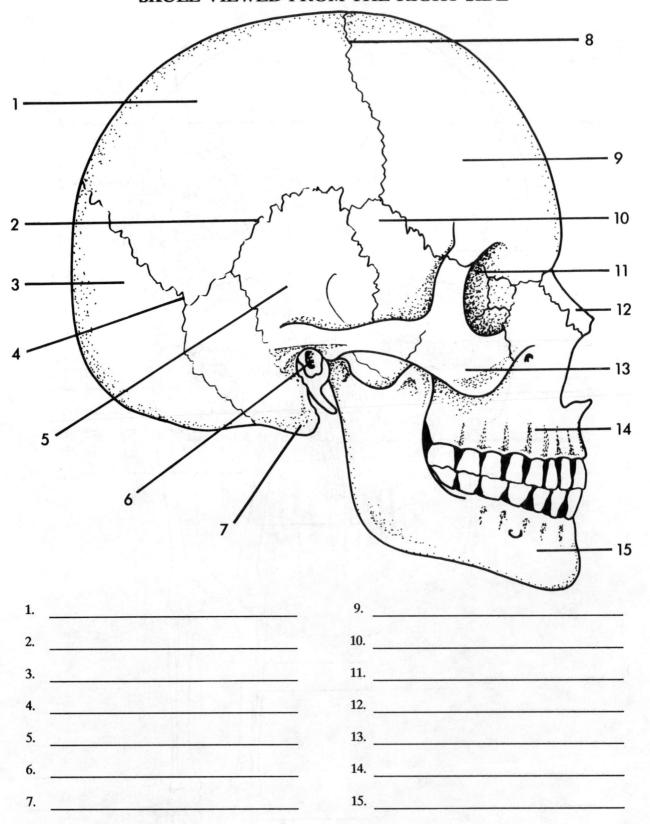

1. _____
2. _____
3. _____
4. _____
5. _____
6. _____
7. _____
8. _____

9. _____
10. _____
11. _____
12. _____
13. _____
14. _____
15. _____

SKULL VIEWED FROM THE FRONT

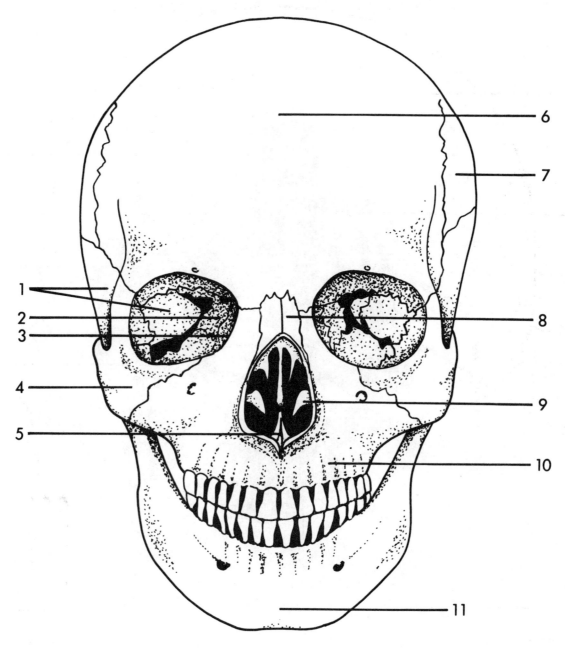

1. _____
2. _____
3. _____
4. _____
5. _____
6. _____

7. _____
8. _____
9. _____
10. _____
11. _____

STRUCTURE OF A DIARTHROTIC JOINT

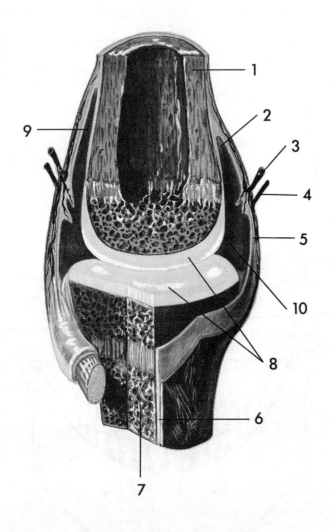

1. _____   6. _____

2. _____   7. _____

3. _____   8. _____

4. _____   9. _____

5. _____   10. _____

CHAPTER 7

The Muscular System

The muscular system is often referred to as the "power system," and rightfully so, because it is this system that provides the motion necessary to move the body and perform organic functions. Just as an automobile relies on the engine to provide motion, the body depends on the muscular system to perform both voluntary and involuntary types of movement. Walking, breathing, and the digestion of food are but a few examples of body functions that require the healthy performance of the muscular system.

Although this system has several functions, the primary purpose is to provide movement or power. Muscles produce power by contracting. The ability of a large muscle or muscle group to contract depends on the ability of microscopic muscle fibers that contract within the larger muscle. An understanding of these microscopic muscle fibers will assist you as you progress in your study to the larger muscles and muscle groups.

Muscle contractions may be one of several types: isotonic, isometric, twitch, or tetanic. When skeletal or voluntary muscles contract, they provide us with a variety of motions. Flexion, extension, abduction, adduction, and rotation are examples of these movements that provide us with both strength and agility.

Muscles must be used to keep the body healthy and in good condition. Scientific evidence keeps pointing to the fact that the proper use and exercise of muscles may improve longevity. An understanding of the structure and function of the muscular system may, therefore, add quality and quantity to our lives.

TOPICS FOR REVIEW

Before progressing to Chapter 8, you should familiarize yourself with the structure and function of the three major types of muscle tissue. Your review should include the microscopic structure of skeletal muscle tissue, how a muscle is stimulated, the major types of skeletal muscle contractions, and the skeletal muscle groups. Your study should conclude with an understanding of the types of movements produced by skeletal muscle contractions and the major muscular disorders.

MUSCLE TISSUE

Select the correct term from the choices given and insert the letter in the answer blank.

(a) Skeletal muscle   (b) Cardiac muscle   (c) Smooth muscle

_____ 1. Striated
_____ 2. Cells branch frequently
_____ 3. Moves food into stomach
_____ 4. Nonstriated
_____ 5. Voluntary
_____ 6. Keeps blood circulating through its vessels
_____ 7. Involuntary
_____ 8. Attaches to bone
_____ 9. Hollow internal organs
_____ 10. Maintenance of normal blood pressure

▶ If you have had difficulty with this section, review page 166. ◀

SKELETAL MUSCLES

Match the term on the left with the proper selection on the right.

Group A

_____11. Origin
_____12. Insertion
_____13. Body
_____14. Tendons
_____15. Bursae

a. The muscle unit excluding the ends
b. Attachment to the more movable bone
c. Fluid-filled sacs
d. Attachment to more stationary bone
e. Attach muscle to bones

MICROSCOPIC STRUCTURE

Group B

_____16. Muscle fibers
_____17. Actin
_____18. Sarcomere
_____19. Myosin
_____20. Myofilament

a. Protein that forms thick myofilaments
b. Basic functional unit of skeletal muscle
c. Protein that forms thin myofilaments
d. Microscopic threadlike structures found in skeletal muscle fibers
e. Specialized contractile cells of muscle tissue

▶ If you have had difficulty with this section, review pages 166-169. ◀

FUNCTIONS

Fill in the blanks.

21. Muscles move bones by _____ on them.

22. As a rule, only the _____ bone moves.

23. The _____ bone moves toward the _____ bone.

24. Of all the muscles contracting simultaneously, the one mainly responsible for producing a particular movement is called the _____ for that movement.

25. As prime movers contract, other muscles called _____ relax.

26. The biceps brachii is the prime mover during flexing, and the brachialis is its helper or _____ muscle.

27. We are able to maintain our body position because of a specialized type of skeletal muscle contraction called _____.

28. _____ maintains body posture by counteracting the pull of gravity.

29. A decrease in temperature, a condition know as _____, will drastically affect cellular activity and normal body function.

30. Energy required to produce a muscle contraction is obtained from _____.

> ► If you have had difficulty with this section, review pages 169-170. ◄

FATIGUE
MOTOR UNIT
MUSCLE STIMULUS

*If the statement is true, write **T** on the answer blank. If the statement is false, correct the statement by circling the incorrect term and inserting the correct term in the answer blank.*

_____ 31. The point of contact between the nerve ending and the muscle fiber is called a motor neuron.

_____ 32. A motor neuron together with the cells it innervates is called a motor unit.

_____ 33. If muscle cells are stimulated repeatedly without adequate periods of rest, the strength of the muscle contraction will decrease resulting in fatigue.

_____ 34. The depletion of oxygen in muscle cells during vigorous and prolonged exercise is known as fatigue.

_____ 35. An adequate stimulus will contract a muscle cell completely because of the "must" theory.

_____ 36. When oxygen supplies run low, muscle cells produce ATP and other waste products during contraction.

_____ 37. Exercise physiologists in the Soviet Union have found that the zero-gravity environment of space promotes a loss of postural drainage.

_____ 38. The minimal level of stimulation required to cause a fiber to contract is called the threshold stimulus.

_____ 39. Smooth muscles bring about movements by pulling on bones across movable joints.

_____ 40. A nervous system disorder that shuts off impulses to certain skeletal muscles may result in paralysis.

TYPES OF SKELETAL MUSCLE CONTRACTION

Circle the correct choice.

41. When a muscle does not shorten and no movement results, the contraction is:

   a. Isometric
   b. Isotonic

   c. Twitch
   d. Tetanic

42. Walking is an example of which type of contraction?

   a. Isometric
   b. Isotonic

   c. Twitch
   d. Tetanic

43. Pushing against a wall is an example of which type of contraction?

   a. Isotonic
   b. Isometric

   c. Twitch
   d. Tetanic

44. Endurance training is also known as:

   a. Isometrics
   b. Hypertrophy

   c. Aerobic training
   d. Strength training

45. Benefits of regular exercise include all of the following *except*:

   a. Improved lung functioning
   b. More efficient heart
   c. Less fatigue
   d. Atrophy

46. Twitch contractions can be easily seen in:

   a. Isolated muscles prepared for research
   b. A great deal of normal muscle activity
   c. During resting periods
   d. None of the above

47. Individual contractions "melt" together to produce a sustained contraction or:

   a. Twitch
   b. Tetanus
   c. Isotonic response
   d. Isometric response

48. In most cases, isotonic contraction of muscle produces movement at a/an:

   a. Insertion
   b. Origin
   c. Joint
   d. Bursa

49. Prolonged inactivity causes muscles to shrink in mass, a condition called:

   a. Hypertrophy
   b. Disuse atrophy
   c. Paralysis
   d. Muscle fatigue

50. Muscle hypertrophy can be best enhanced by a program of:

   a. Isotonic exercise
   b. Better posture
   c. High-protein diet
   d. Strength training

► If you have had difficulty with this section, review pages 171-174. ◄

SKELETAL MUSCLE GROUPS

Choose the proper function for the muscles listed below and place the letter in the answer blank.

(a) Flexor   (b) Extensor   (c) Abductor   (d) Adductor
(e) Rotator   (f) Dorsiflexor or Plantar flexor

_____ 51. Deltoid
_____ 52. Tibialis anterior
_____ 53. Gastrocnemius
_____ 54. Biceps brachii
_____ 55. Gluteus medius
_____ 56. Soleus
_____ 57. Iliopsoas
_____ 58. Pectoralis major
_____ 59. Gluteus maximus
_____ 60. Triceps brachii
_____ 61. Sternocleidomastoid
_____ 62. Trapezius
_____ 63. Gracilis

▸ If you have had difficulty with this section, review page 174-183. ◂

TYPES OF MOVEMENTS PRODUCED BY SKELETAL MUSCLE CONTRACTIONS

Circle the correct choice.

64. A movement that makes the angle between two bones smaller is:

   a. Flexion
   b. Extension

   c. Abduction
   d. Adduction

65. Moving a part toward the midline is:

   a. Flexion
   b. Extension

   c. Abduction
   d. Adduction

66. Moving a part away from the midline is:

   a. Flexion
   b. Extension

   c. Abduction
   d. Adduction

67. When you move your head from side to side as in shaking your head "no" you are _____ a muscle group.

   a. Rotating
   b. Pronating

   c. Supinating
   d. Abducting

68. _____ occurs when you turn the palm of your hand from an anterior to posterior position.

   a. Dorsiflexion
   b. Plantar flexion

   c. Supination
   d. Pronation

69. Dorsiflexion refers to:

   a. Hand movements
   b. Eye movements

   c. Foot movements
   d. Head movements

▸ If you have had difficulty with this section, review pages 181-183. ◂

MAJOR MUSCULAR DISORDERS

Circle the correct answer.

70. Muscle strains are characterized by (myalgia or fibromyositis).

71. Crush injuries can cause (hemoglobin or myoglobin) to accumulate in the blood and result in kidney failure.

72. A viral infection of the nerves that controls skeletal muscle movement is known as (poliomyelitis or muscular dystrophy).

73. (Muscular dystrophy or Myasthenia gravis) is a group of genetic diseases characterized by atrophy of skeletal muscle tissues.

74. (Muscular dystrophy or Myasthenia gravis) is an autoimmune disease in which the immune system attacks muscle cells at the neuromuscular junction.

▶ If you have difficulty with this section, review pages 184-186. ◀

APPLYING WHAT YOU KNOW

75. Casey noticed pain whenever she reached for anything in her cupboards. Her doctor told her that the small fluid-filled sacs in her shoulder were inflamed. What condition did Casey have?

76. The nurse was preparing an injection for Mrs. Tatakis. The amount to be given was 2 ml. What area of the body will the nurse most likely select for this injection?

77. Warren was playing football and pulled a band of fibrous connective tissue that attached a muscle to a bone. What is the common term for this tissue?

78. **WORD FIND**

Can you find the muscles from the list below in the box of letters? Words may be spelled top to bottom, bottom to top, right to left, left to right, or diagonally.

```
U X D T F I N I G I R O I R G G X F Z B
K P B F L D N K Y D X S O N W R W Q N U
E I Z H M U S C L E O T O M R O E T O Z
J S R I Q E U V I T C I J G O M D E I Y
W P D R X M G S O U X J X D T R E N X G
K E N B K O D N D E U G C E A N G O E F
M C M A X I I B L N T U D T T I S S L F
S I Y M K C A F P S S T M A O B U Y F N
Z B V H P E I W L N Y E G I R U I N R O
P H S X X S B H S F H X A R F R Z O S I
G W V V R B G S O C P T R T F S E V P T
F Z W O K Q E N L O O E H S N A P I E R
A M D X E P M W E H R N P U D I A T C E
G F Y R S T O A U Q T S A Z Q H R I I S
C R Z A A N R C S E A I I E P G T S R N
U B H J H S M V N N L O D V G C T T T I
G H T S I G R E N Y S N D I O T L E D V
I S O M E T R I C Z K G E U G I T A F U
I S C Y S U I M E N C O R T S A G C Z A
T C S G N I R T S M A H R T E N D O N H
```

LIST OF WORDS

ORIGIN	TRICEPS	ISOTONIC
EXTENSION	TRAPEZIUS	BICEPS
ABDUCTOR	DELTOID	SYNERGIST
DORSIFLEXION	HAMSTRINGS	DIAPHRAGM
STRIATED	ATROPHY	GASTROCNEMIUS
BURSA	TENDON	TENOSYNOVITIS
FATIGUE	INSERTION	FLEXION
ROTATOR	SOLEUS	ISOMETRIC
MUSCLE		

DID YOU KNOW?

If all of your muscles pulled in one direction, you would have the power to move 25 tons.

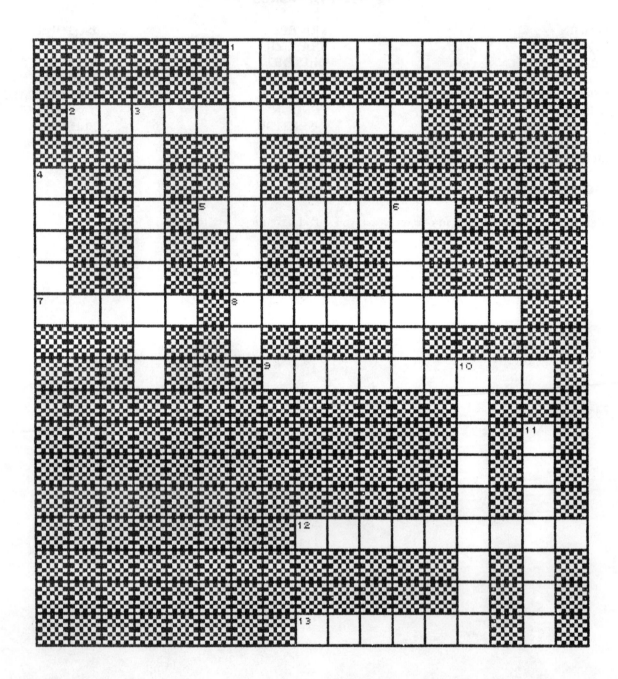

ACROSS

1. Away from the body's midline
2. Increase in size
5. Shaking your head "no"
7. Protein which composes myofilaments
8. Assist prime movers with movement
9. Movement that makes joint angles larger
12. Toward the body's midline
13. Anchors muscles to bones

DOWN

1. Produces movement opposite to prime movers
3. Turning your palm from an anterior to posterior position
4. Small fluid-filled sacs between tendons and bones
6. Attachment to the more stationary bone
10. Attachment to the more movable bone
11. Muscle shrinkage

MUSCLES—ANTERIOR VIEW

1. _____
2. _____
3. _____
4. _____
5. _____
6. _____
7. _____
8. _____
9. _____
10. _____
11. _____
12. _____
13. _____
14. _____
15. _____
16. _____
17. _____
18. _____

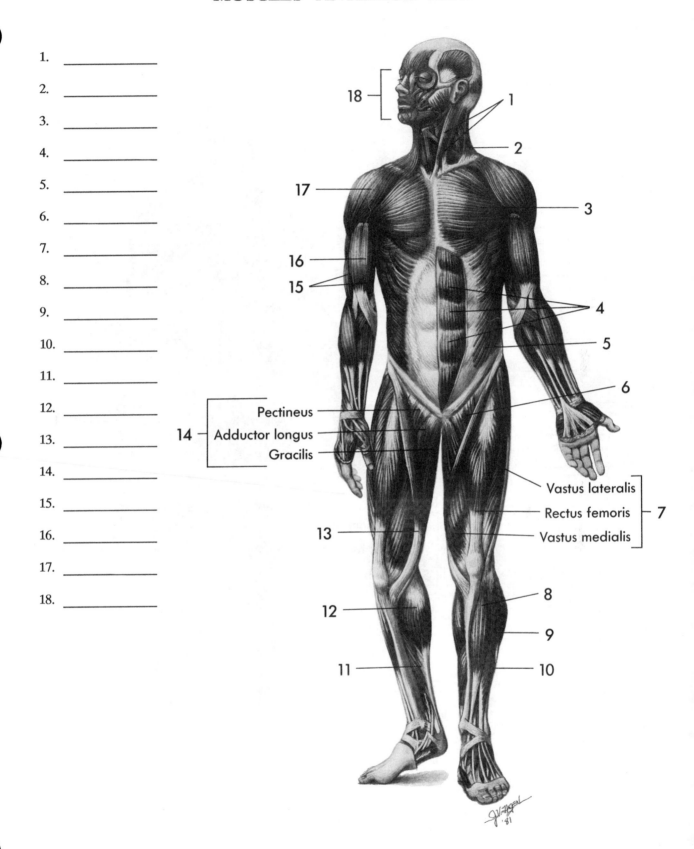

18
1
2
17
16
15
3
4
5
6
14 — Pectineus
Adductor longus
Gracilis
Vastus lateralis
Rectus femoris
Vastus medialis
7
13
12
8
9
11
10

69

MUSCLES—POSTERIOR VIEW

1. _____
2. _____
3. _____
4. _____
5. _____
6. _____
7. _____
8. _____
9. _____
10. _____
11. _____
12. _____
13. _____

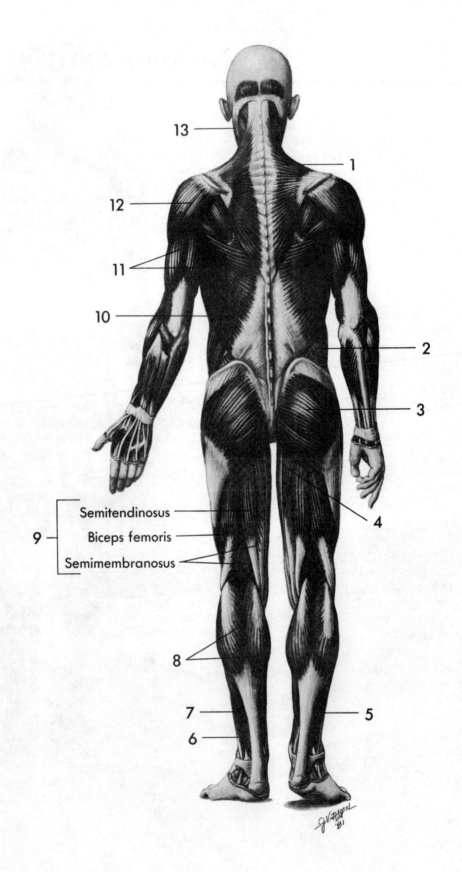

13
1
12
11
10
2
3
4

9 ⎱ Semitendinosus
  ⎰ Biceps femoris
    Semimembranosus

8

7   5
6

CHAPTER 8

The Nervous System

The nervous system organizes and coordinates the millions of impulses received each day to make communication with and enjoyment of our environment possible. The functioning unit of the nervous system is the neuron. Three types of neurons, sensory, motor, and interneurons, exist and are classified according to the direction in which they transmit impulses. Nerve impulses travel over routes made up of neurons and provide the rapid communication that is necessary for maintaining life. The central nervous system is made up of the spinal cord and brain. The spinal cord provides access to and from the brain by means of ascending and descending tracts. In addition, the spinal cord functions as the primary reflex center of the body. The brain can be subdivided for easier learning into the brain stem, cerebellum, diencephalon, and cerebrum. These areas provide the extraordinary network necessary to receive, interpret, and respond to the simplest or most complex impulses.

While you concentrate on this chapter, your body is performing a multitude of functions. Fortunately for us, the beating of the heart, the digestion of food, breathing, and most of our other day-to-day processes do not require our supervision or thought. They function automatically, and the division of the nervous system that regulates these functions is known as the autonomic nervous system.

The autonomic nervous system consists of two divisions called the sympathetic system and the parasympathetic system. The sympathetic system functions as an emergency system and prepares us for "fight" or "flight." The parasympathetic system dominates control of many visceral effectors under normal everyday conditions. Together, these two divisions regulate the body's automatic functions in an effort to assist with the maintenance of homeostasis. Your understanding of this chapter will alert you to the complexity and functions of the nervous system and the "automatic pilot" of your body—the autonomic system.

TOPICS FOR REVIEW

Before progressing to Chapter 9, you should review the organs and divisions of the nervous system, the structure and function of the major types of cells in this system, the structure and function of a reflex arc, and the transmission of nerve impulses. Your study should include the anatomy and physiology of the brain and spinal cord and the nerves that extend from these two areas.

Finally, an understanding of the autonomic nervous system, the specific functions of the subdivisions of this system, and the major disorders of the nervous system are necessary to complete the review of this chapter.

ORGANS AND DIVISIONS OF THE NERVOUS SYSTEM
CELLS OF THE NERVOUS SYSTEM

Match the term on the left with the proper selection on the right.

Group A

_____ 1. Sense organ
_____ 2. Central nervous system
_____ 3. Peripheral nervous system
_____ 4. Autonomic nervous system

a. Subdivision of peripheral nervous system
b. Ear
c. Brain and spinal cord
d. Nerves that extend to the outlying parts of the body

Group B

_____ 5. Dendrite
_____ 6. Schwann cell
_____ 7. Motor neuron
_____ 8. Nodes of Ranvier
_____ 9. Fascicles
_____ 10. Epineurium

a. Indentations between adjacent Schwann cells
b. Branching projection of neuron
c. Also known as efferent
d. Forms myelin outside the CNS
e. Tough sheath that covers the whole nerve
f. Groups of wrapped axons

CELLS OF NERVOUS SYSTEM

Select the best choice for the following words and insert the correct letter in the answer blank.

(a) Neurons

(b) Neuroglia

_____ 11. Axon
_____ 12. Connective tissue
_____ 13. Astrocytes
_____ 14. Sensory
_____ 15. Conduct impulses
_____ 16. Forms the myelin sheath around central nerve fibers
_____ 17. Phagocytosis
_____ 18. Efferent
_____ 19. Multiple sclerosis
_____ 20. Neurilemma

▶ If you have had difficulty with this section, review pages 194-198. ◀

REFLEX ARCS

Fill in the blanks.

21. The simplest kind of reflex arc is a _____.

22. Three-neuron arcs consist of all three kinds of neurons, _____, _____, and _____.

23. Impulse conduction in a reflex arc normally starts in _____.

24. A _____ is the microscopic space that separates the axon of one neuron from the dendrites of another neuron.

25. A _____ is the response to impulse conduction over reflex arcs.

26. Contraction of a muscle that causes it to pull away from an irritating stimulus is known as the

_____.

27. _____ _____ provides a more rapid type of impulse travel than is possible in nonmyelinated sections.

28. All _____ lie entirely within the gray matter of the central nervous system.

29. In a patellar reflex, the nerve impulses that reach the quadriceps muscle (the effector) result in the classic

_____ response.

30. _____ forms the H-shaped inner core of the spinal cord.

► If you have had difficulty with this section, review pages 199-200. ◄

NERVE IMPULSES

Circle the correct answer.

31. Nerve impulses (do or do not) continually race along every nerve cell's surface.

32. When a stimulus acts on a neuron, it (increases or decreases) the permeability of the stimulated point of its membrane to sodium ions.

33. An inward movement of positive ions leaves a/an (lack or excess) of negative ions outside.

34. The plasma membrane of the (presynaptic neuron or postsynaptic neuron) makes up a portion of the synapse.

35. A synaptic knob is a tiny bulge at the end of the (presynaptic or postsynaptic) neuron's axon.

36. Acetylcholine is an example of a (neurotransmitter or protein molecule receptor).

37. Neurotransmitters are chemicals that allow neurons to (communicate or reproduce) with one another.

38. Neurotransmitters are distributed (randomly or specifically) into groups of neurons.

39. Catecholamines may play a role in (sleep or reproduction).

40. Endorphins and enkephalins are neurotransmitters that inhibit conduction of (fear or pain) impulses.

► If you have had difficulty with this section, review pages 201-204. ◄

DIVISIONS OF THE BRAIN

Circle the correct choice.

41. The portion of the brain stem that joins the spinal cord to the brain is the:

    a. Pons
    b. Cerebellum
    c. Diencephalon
    d. Hypothalamus
    e. Medulla

42. Which one of the following is *not* a function of the brain stem?

    a. Conducts sensory impulses from the spinal cord to the higher centers of the brain.
    b. Conducts motor impulses from the cerebrum to the spinal cord.
    c. Controls heartbeat, respiration, and blood vessel diameter.
    d. Contains centers for speech and memory.

43. Which one of the following is *not* part of the diencephalon?

    a. Cerebrum
    b. Thalamus
    c. Pituitary gland
    d. Third ventricle gray matter

44. ADH is produced by the:

    a. Pituitary gland
    b. Medulla
    c. Mammillary bodies
    d. Third ventricle
    e. Hypothalamus

45. Which one of the following is *not* a function of the hypothalamus?

    a. It controls the rate of heartbeat.
    b. It controls the constriction and dilation of blood vessels.
    c. It controls the contraction of the stomach and intestines.
    d. It produces releasing hormones that affect the posterior pituitary.
    e. All of the above are functions of the hypothalamus.

46. Which one of the following parts of the brain helps in the association of sensations with emotions, as well as aiding in the arousal or alerting mechanism?

    a. Pons
    b. Hypothalamus
    c. Cerebellum
    d. Thalamus
    e. None of the above is correct

47. Which of the following is *not* true of the cerebrum?

    a. Its lobes correspond to the bones that lie over them.
    b. Its grooves are called gyri.
    c. Most of its gray matter lies on the surface of the cerebrum.
    d. Its outer region is called the cerebral cortex.
    e. Its two hemispheres are connected by a structure called the corpus callosum.

48. Which one of the following is *not* a function of the cerebrum?

   a. Willed movement
   b. Consciousness
   c. Memory
   d. Conscious awareness of sensations
   e. All of the above are functions of the cerebrum

49. The area of the cerebrum responsible for the perception of sound lies in the _____ lobe.

   a. Frontal
   b. Temporal

   c. Occipital
   d. Parietal

50. Visual perception is located in the _____ lobe.

   a. Frontal
   b. Temporal
   c. Parietal

   d. Occipital
   e. None of the above is correct

51. Which one of the following is *not* a function of the cerebellum?

   a. Maintains equilibrium
   b. Helps produce smooth, coordinated movements
   c. Helps maintain normal postures
   d. Associates sensations with emotions

52. Within the interior of the cerebrum are a few islands of gray matter known as:

   a. Fissures
   b. Basal ganglia

   c. Gyri
   d. Myelin

53. A cerebrovascular accident is commonly referred to as (a)

   a. Stroke
   b. Parkinson's disease

   c. Tumor
   d. Multiple sclerosis

54. Parkinson's disease is a disease of the:

   a. Myelin
   b. Axons

   c. Neuroglia
   d. Basal ganglia

55. The largest section of the brain is the

   a. Cerebellum
   b. Pons

   c. Cerebrum
   d. Midbrain

▶ If you have had difficulty with this section, review pages 208-210. ◀

BRAIN DISORDERS

Select the best choice and insert the correct letter in the answer blank.

a. SPECT
b. MRI
c. CT
d. Hemiplegia
e. Cerebral palsy

f. EEG
g. Huntington's disease
h. CVA
i. Dementia
j. PET

_____56. Stroke
_____57. Paralysis of one side of the body
_____58. Crippling disease that involves permanent, nonprogressive damage to motor control areas of the brain
_____59. Imaging technique for brain which involves scanning the head with a revolving x-ray generator
_____60. Scanning method that determines the functional characteristics of the brain by introducing a radioactive substance into the blood supply of the brain
_____61. Used to visualize blood flow in brain
_____62. Scanning method that uses a magnetic field to induce brain tissues to emit radio waves
_____63. Measurement of electrical activity of the brain
_____64. Characteristic of Alzheimer's disease
_____65. Inherited disease characterized by chorea

▶ If you have had difficulty with this section, review pages 210-212. ◀

SPINAL CORD

*If the statement is true, write **T** on the answer blank. If the statement is false, correct the statement by circling the incorrect term and inserting the correct term in the answer blank.*

_____66. The spinal cord is approximately 24 to 25 inches long.
_____67. The spinal cord ends at the bottom of the sacrum.
_____68. The extension of the meninges beyond the cord is convenient for performing CAT scans without danger of injuring the spinal cord.
_____69. Bundles of myelinated nerve fibers—dendrites—make up the white outer columns of the spinal cord.
_____70. Ascending tracts conduct impulses up the cord to the brain and descending tracts conduct impulses down the cord from the brain.
_____71. Tracts are functional organizations in that all the axons that compose a tract serve several functions.
_____72. A loss of sensation caused by a spinal cord injury is called paralysis.

▶ If you have had difficulty with this section, review pages 212-215. ◀

COVERINGS AND FLUID SPACES OF BRAIN AND SPINAL CORD

Circle the one that does not belong.

73. Meniges   Pia mater   Ventricles   Dura mater

74. Arachnoid   Middle layer   CSF   Cobweblike

75.	CSF	Ventricles	Subarachnoid space	Pia mater
76.	Tough	Vertebral canal	Dura mater	Choroid plexus
77.	Brain tumor	Subarachnoid space	CSF	Fourth lumbar vertebra

CRANIAL NERVES

78. *Fill in the missing areas on the chart below.*

NERVE		CONDUCT IMPULSES	FUNCTION
I		From nose to brain	Sense of smell
II	Optic	From eye to brain	
III	Oculomotor		Eye movements
IV		From brain to external eye muscles	Eye movements
V	Trigeminal	From skin and mucous membrane of head and from teeth to brain; also from brain to chewing muscles	
VI	Abducens		Turning eyes outward
VII	Facial	From taste buds of tongue to brain; from brain to face muscles	
VIII		From ear to brain	Hearing; sense of balance
IX	Glossopharyngeal		Sensations of throat, taste, swallowing movements, secretion of saliva
X		From throat, larynx, and organs in thoracic and abdominal cavities to brain; also from brain to muscles of throat and to organs in thoracic and abdominal cavities	Sensations of throat, larynx, and of thoracic and abdominal organs; swallowing, voice production, slowing of heartbeat, acceleration of peristalsis (gut movements)
XI	Spinal accessory	From brain to certain shoulder and neck muscles	
XII		From brain to muscles of tongue	Tongue movements

▸ If you have had difficulty with this section, review page 221, Table 8-2. ◂

CRANIAL NERVES
SPINAL NERVES

Select the best choice for the following words and insert the correct letter in the answer blank.

(a) Cranial nerves   (b) Spinal nerves

_____79. 12 pairs
_____80. Dermatome
_____81. Vagus
_____82. Shingles
_____83. 31 pairs
_____84. Optic
_____85. C1
_____86. Plexus

▸ If you have had difficulty with this section, review pages 219-222. ◂

DEFINITIONS
NAMES OF DIVISIONS

Match the term on the left with the proper selection on the right.

_____87. Autonomic nervous system
_____88. Autonomic neurons
_____89. Preganglionic neurons
_____90. Visceral effectors
_____91. Sympathetic system
_____92. Somatic nervous system

a. Divisions of ANS
b. Tissues to which autonomic neurons conduct impulses
c. Voluntary actions
d. Regulates body's involuntary functions
e. Motor neurons that make up the ANS
f. Conduct impulses between the spinal cord and a ganglion

SYMPATHETIC NERVOUS SYSTEM
PARASYMPATHETIC NERVOUS SYSTEM

Circle the correct choice.

93. Dendrites and cell bodies of sympathetic preganglionic neurons are located in the:

a. Brain stem and sacral portion of the spinal cord
b. Sympathetic ganglia
c. Gray matter of the thoracic and upper lumbar segments of the spinal cord
d. Ganglia close to effectors

Unscramble the words.

116. RONNESU
☐☐☐☐☐☐◯

117. APSYENS
☐◯☐◯☐◯☐

118. CIATUNOMO
☐☐☐◯☐☐◯☐☐

119. SHTOMO   ULMSEC
☐☐☐☐◯◯   ☐☐☐◯☐◯

Take the circled letters, unscramble them, and fill in the statement.

What the man hoped the IRS agent would be during his audit.

120. ☐☐☐☐☐☐☐☐☐☐☐☐

APPLYING WHAT YOU KNOW

121. Mr. Hemstreet suffered a cerebrovascular accident and it was determined that the damage affected the left side of his cerebrum. On which side of his body will he most likely notice any paralysis?

122. Baby Hansen was born with an excessive accumulation of cerebrospinal fluid in the ventricles. A catheter was placed in the ventricle and the fluid was drained by means of a shunt into the circulatory bloodstream. What condition does this medical history describe?

123. Mrs. Gordon looked out her window to see a man trapped under the wheel of a car. Although slightly built, Mrs. Gordon rushed to the car, lifted it, and saved the man underneath the wheel. What division of the autonomic nervous system made this seemingly impossible task possible?

124. Cassidy's heart raced and her palms became clammy as she watched the monster at the local theater. When the movie was over, however, she told her friends that she was not afraid at all. She appeared to be as calm as before the movie. What division of the autonomic nervous system made this possible?

125. Bill was going to his boss for his annual evaluation. He is planning to ask for a raise and hopes the evaluation will be good. Which subdivision of the autonomic nervous system will be active during this conference? Should he have a large meal before his appointment? Support your answer with facts from the chapter.

DID YOU KNOW?

Although all pain is felt and interpreted in the brain, it has no pain sensation itself—even when cut!

THE NERVOUS SYSTEM

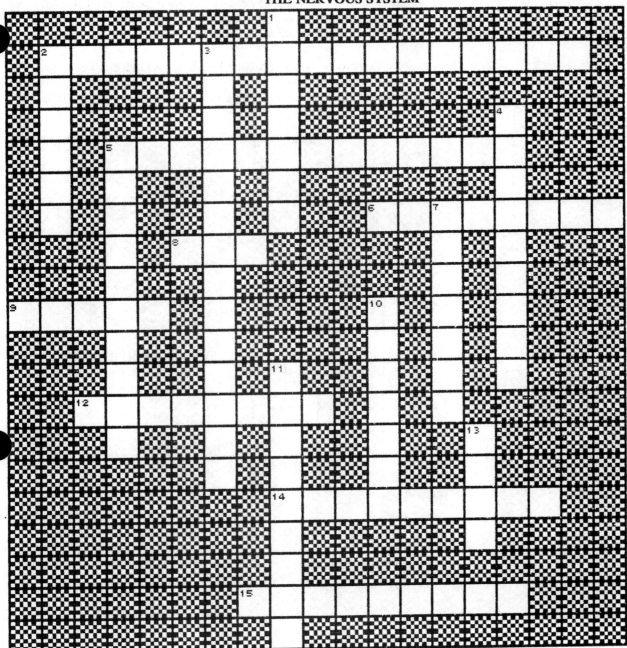

ACROSS

2. Myelin disorder
5. Neurotransmitter
6. Cluster of nerve cell bodies outside the central nervous system
8. Peripheral nervous system (abbrev.)
9. Bundle of axons located within the CNS
12. Pia mater
14. Peripheral beginning of a sensory neuron's dendrite
15. Astrocytes

DOWN

1. Area of the brain stem
2. Fatty substance found around some nerve fibers
3. Neurons that conduct impulses from a ganglion
4. Two neuron arc
5. Neuroglia
7. Nerve cells
10. Where impulses are transmitted from one neuron to another
11. Transmits impulses toward the cell body
13. Transmits impulses away from the cell body

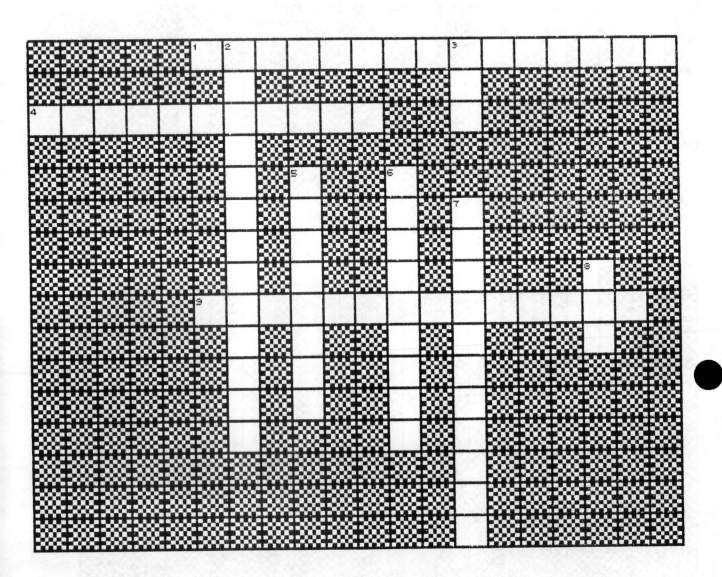

ACROSS

1. System that controls visceral effectors under normal conditions
4. Type of fibers which release acetylcholine
9. Adrenergic fibers release this neurotransmitter

DOWN

2. Neurotransmitter released by cholinergic fibers
3. Autonomic nervous system (abbrev.)
5. Type of effect which is autonomic
6. Also known as visceral effectors
7. System that functions as an emergency one
8. Parasympathetic nervous system (abbrev.)

NEURON

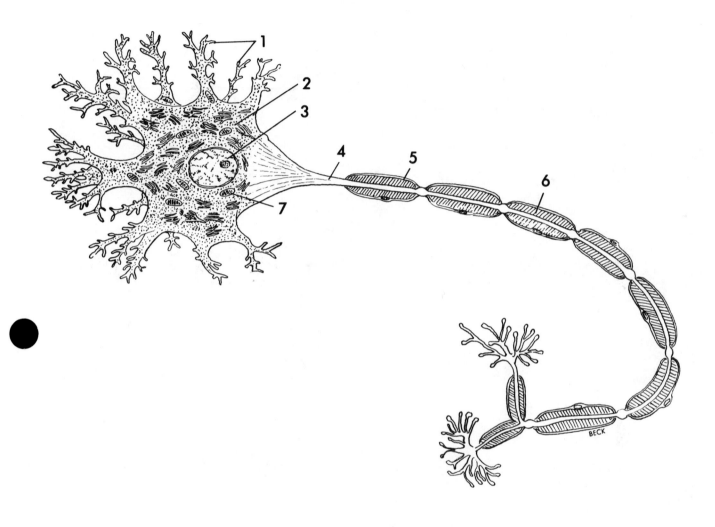

1. _____

2. _____

3. _____

4. _____

5. _____

6. _____

7. _____

CROSS-SECTION OF SPINAL CORD

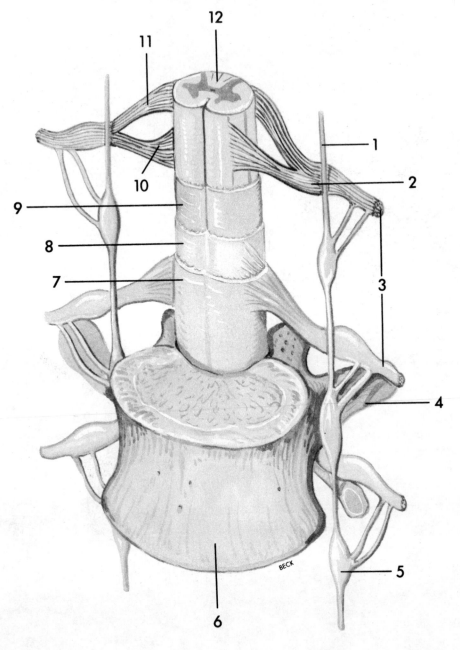

BECK

1. _____

2. _____

3. _____

4. _____

5. _____

6. _____

7. _____

8. _____

9. _____

10. _____

11. _____

12. _____

NEURAL PATHWAY INVOLVED IN THE PATELLAR REFLEX

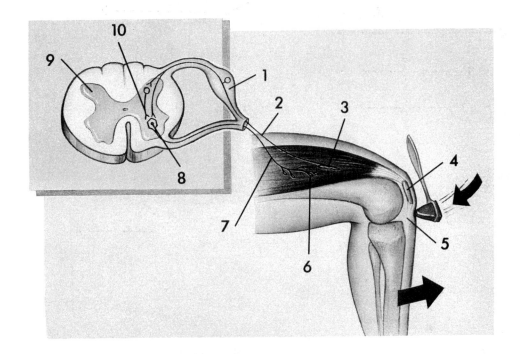

1. _____
2. _____
3. _____
4. _____
5. _____

6. _____
7. _____
8. _____
9. _____
10. _____

THE CEREBRUM

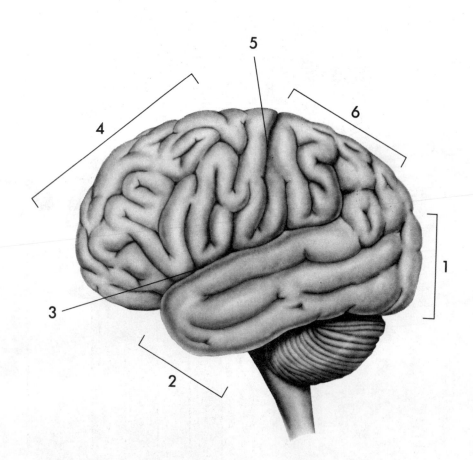

1. _____

2. _____

3. _____

4. _____

5. _____

6. _____

SAGITTAL SECTION OF THE CENTRAL NERVOUS SYSTEM

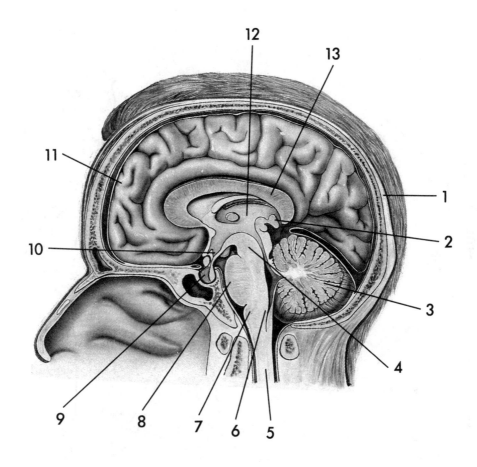

1. _____

2. _____

3. _____

4. _____

5. _____

6. _____

6. _____

7. _____

8. _____

9. _____

10._____

11._____

NEURON PATHWAYS

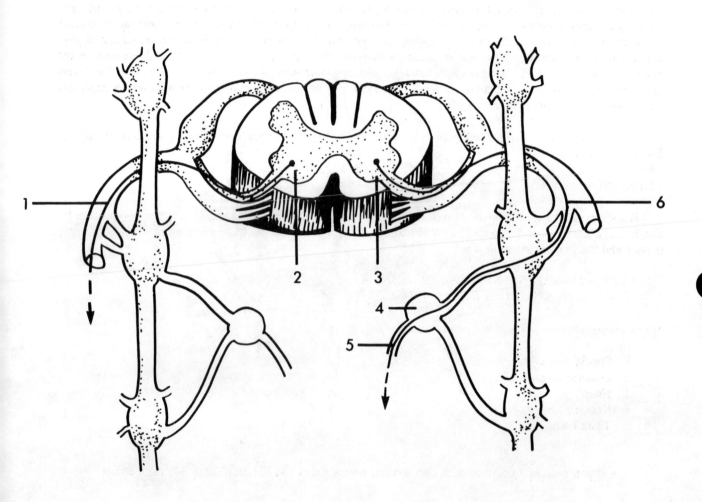

1. _____
2. _____
3. _____

4. _____
5. _____
6. _____

CHAPTER 9

The Senses

Consider this scene for a moment. You are walking along a beautiful beach watching the sunset. You notice the various hues and are amazed at the multitude of shades that cover the sky. The waves are indeed melodious as they splash along the shore and you wiggle your feet with delight as you sense the warm, soft sand trickling between your toes. You sip on a soda and then inhale the fresh salt air as you continue your stroll along the shore. It is a memorable scene, but one that would not be possible without the assistance of your sense organs. The sense organs pick up messages that are sent over nerve pathways to specialized areas in the brain for interpretation. They make communication with and enjoyment of the environment possible. The visual, auditory, tactile, olfactory, and gustatory sense organs not only protect us from danger but also add an important dimension to our daily pleasures of life.

Your study of this chapter will give you an understanding of another one of the systems necessary for homeostasis and survival.

TOPICS FOR REVIEW

Before progressing to Chapter 10, you should review the classification of sense organs and the process for converting a stimulus into a sensation. Your study should also include an understanding of the special sense organs and the general sense organs.

CLASSIFICATION OF SENSE ORGANS
CONVERTING A STIMULUS INTO A SENSATION

Match the term on the left with the proper selection on the right.

D	1. Special sense organ	a.	Olfactory cells
E	2. General sense organ	b.	Meissner's corpuscles
B	3. Nose	c.	Chemoreceptor
C	4. Krause's end-bulbs	d.	Eye
A	5. Taste buds	e.	Touch

▸ If you have had difficulty with this section, review pages 236-237 and Table 9-2, page 252. ◂

SPECIAL SENSE ORGANS

Eye

Circle the correct choice.

6. The "white" of the eye is more commonly called the:

a. Choroid
b. Cornea
c. Sclera

d. Retina
e. None of the above is correct

7. The "colored" part of the eye is known as the:

   a. Retina
   b. Cornea
   c. Pupil
   d. Sclera
   e. Iris

8. The transparent portion of the sclera, referred to as the "window" of the eye, is the:

   a. Retina
   b. Cornea
   c. Pupil
   d. Iris

9. The mucous membrane that covers the front of the eye is called the:

   a. Cornea
   b. Choroid
   c. Conjunctiva
   d. Ciliary body
   e. None of the above is correct

10. The structure that can contract or dilate to allow more or less light to enter the eye is the:

    a. Lens
    b. Choroid
    c. Retina
    d. Cornea
    e. Iris

11. When the eye is looking at objects far in the distance, the lens is _____ and the ciliary muscle is _____.

    a. Rounded, contracted
    b. Rounded, relaxed
    c. Slightly rounded, contracted
    d. Slightly curved, relaxed
    e. None of the above is correct

12. The lens of the eye is held in place by the:

    a. Ciliary muscle
    b. Aqueous humor
    c. Vitreous humor
    d. Cornea

13. When the lens loses its elasticity and can no longer bring near objects into focus, the condition is known as:

    a. Glaucoma
    b. Presbyopia
    c. Astigmatism
    d. Strabismus

14. The fluid in front of the lens that is constantly being formed, drained, and replaced in the anterior cavity is the:

    a. Vitreous humor
    b. Protoplasm
    c. Aqueous humor
    d. Conjunctiva

15. If drainage of the aqueous humor is blocked, the internal pressure within the eye will increase and a condition known as _____ could occur.

    a. Presbyopia
    b. Glaucoma
    c. Color blindness
    d. Cataracts

92

16. The rods and cones are the visual receptors and are located on the:

    a. Sclera
    b. Cornea
    c. Choroid
    d. Retina

17. Photoreception is the sense of:

    a. Vision
    b. Smell
    c. Taste
    d. Balance

18. If our eyes are abnormally elongated, the image focuses in front of the retina and a condition known as _____ occurs.

    a. Hyperopia
    b. Cataracts
    c. Night blindness
    d. Myopia

▸ If you have had difficulty with this section, review pages 236-240. ◂

VISUAL DISORDERS

Select the best answer from the choices given and insert the letter in the answer blank.

a. Strabismus
b. Retinopathy
c. Myopia
d. Glaucoma
e. Astigmatism
f. Conjunctivitis
g. Nyctalopia
h. Hyperopia
i. Scotoma
j. Cataracts

___C___ 19. Nearsightedness
___E___ 20. An irregularity in the cornea
___F___ 21. "Pink-eye"
___A___ 22. "Cross-eyes"
___J___ 23. Cloudy spots in the eye's lens
___B___ 24. Often caused by diabetes mellitus
___H___ 25. Farsightedness
___G___ 26. "Night blindness"
___I___ 27. Loss of only the center of the visual field
___D___ 28. Excessive intraocular pressure caused by abnormal accumulation of aqueous humor

▸ If you have had difficulty with this section, review pages 239-244. ◂

Ear

Select the best answer from the choices given and insert the letter in the answer blank.

(a) External ear   (b) Middle ear   (c) Inner ear

_____ 29. Malleus
_____ 30. Perilymph
_____ 31. Incus
_____ 32. Ceruminous glands

_____33. Cochlea
_____34. Auditory canal
_____35. Semicircular canals
_____36. Stapes
_____37. Tympanic membrane
_____38. Organ of Corti

Fill in the blanks.

39. The external ear has two parts: the _____ and the

    _____ .

40. Another name for the tympanic membrane is the _____ .

41. The bones of the middle ear are referred to, collectively, as _____ .

42. The stapes presses against a membrane that covers a small opening, the _____

    _____ .

43. A middle ear infection is called _____ _____ .

44. The _____ is located adjacent to the oval window between the semicircular canals and
    the cochlea.

45. Located within the semicircular canals and the vestibule are _____ for balance and equilibrium.

46. The sensory cells in the _____ _____ are stimulated when movement of
    the head causes the endolymph to move.

▸ If you have had difficulty with this section, review pages 244-247. ◂

HEARING DISORDERS

Selection the best answer from the choices given and insert the letter in the answer blank.

a. Tinnitus
b. Presbycusis
c. Otosclerosis

d. Otitis media
e. Mastoiditis
f. Meniere's disease

_____47. Inherited bone disorder which impairs conduction by causing structural irregularities in the stapes.
_____48. "Ringing in the ear"
_____49. Middle ear infection
_____50. Untreated otitis media can lead to this condition
_____51. Progressive hearing loss associated with aging
_____52. Chronic inner ear disease characterized by progressive nerve deafness and vertigo

▸ If you had difficulty with this section, review pages 247-248. ◂

TASTE RECEPTORS
SMELL RECEPTORS
GENERAL SENSE ORGANS

Circle the correct answer.

53. Structures known as (papillae or olfactory cells) are found on the tongue.

54. Nerve impulses generated by stimulation of taste buds travel primarily through two (cranial or spinal) nerves.

55. To be detected by olfactory receptors chemicals must be dissolved in the watery (mucus or plasma) that lines the nasal cavity.

56. The pathways taken by olfactory nerve impulses and the areas where these impulses are interpreted are closely associated with areas of the brain important in (hearing or memory).

57. A sense of position and movement is known as (proprioception or mechanoreception).

> ▸ If you have had difficulty with this section, review pages 249-250. ◂

APPLYING WHAT YOU KNOW

58. Mr. Nay was an avid swimmer and competed regularly in his age group. He had to withdraw from the last competition due to an infection of his ear. Antibiotics and analgesics were prescribed by the doctor. What is the medical term for his condition?

59. Mrs. Metheny loved the out-of-doors and spent a great deal of her spare time basking in the sun on the beach. Her physician suggested that she begin wearing sunglasses regularly when he noticed milky spots beginning to appear on Mrs. Metheny's lenses. What condition was Mrs. Metheny's physician trying to prevent from occurring?

60. Amanda repeatedly became ill with throat infections during her first few years of school. Lately, however, she has noticed that whenever she has a throat infection, her ears become very sore also. What might be the cause of this additional problem?

61. Jeremy was hit in the nose with a baseball during practice. His sense of smell was temporarily gone. What nerve receptors were damaged during the injury?

62. WORD FIND

Can you find the terms from this chapter listed below in the box of letters? Words may be spelled top to bottom, bottom to top, right to left, left to right, or diagonally.

```
R C O Y P J A V I T C N U J N O C M X P
B R R O S S U C N I R D A O F X M Y I L
O L F A C T O R Y A R X S M F N X H V H
I R Y G F I Y T N K H B L W P A S E S J
V C A T A R A C T S X P K H P I Z N L A
G U S T A T O R Y B I Z O Y M H T T Y Q
Y Y H P A P I L L A E T A R D C X N J S
U Y T D L N C E L E O I E Q P A S W L O
V O C O C H L E A P P C E S E T X W D C
J C E R U M E N I O E U X E J S E A J C
Y G A E F Y X G Y P R D G N W U N V L F
X C O N E S M B T X R B X S A E J V Q E
H T M Y D E S O A I P O R E P Y H W E Z
Y W V N N E R J D P E A A S R F V A F S
S I Z T R S W H W C V Z I Q X H H K J O
I I R P M E C H A N O R E C E P T O R S
N O I T C A R F E R R N G Q Q E Y E W A
K S A W J A M T M X E W M S Q V F D R T
P J U G L G R O D S V C U G A A G N F R
E S Z I W Y T L G Q I M C A N F F C Q M
```

LIST OF WORDS

SENSES ✓
CONJUNCTIVA ✓
CONES ✓
REFRACTION ✓
CERUMEN (wax) ✓
EUSTACHIAN
OLFACTORY ✓ (smell)

RECEPTORS ✓
PRESBYOPIA ✓
PHOTOPIGMENT ✓
MECHANORECEPTORS ✓
INCUS ✓
GUSTATORY ✓ (Taste)

EYE ✓
RODS ✓
CATARACTS ✓
HYPEROPIA ✓
COCHLEA ✓
PAPILLAE ✓

HYPEROPIA — refractive disorder of the eye caused by a shorter than normal eyeball; farsightedness

PRESBYOPIA — farsightedness of old age

PHOTOPIGMENTS - chemicals in retinal cells that are sensitive to light

MECHANORECEPTORS - receptors that are mechanical in nature; e.g equilibrium and balance sensors in the ear.

THE SENSES

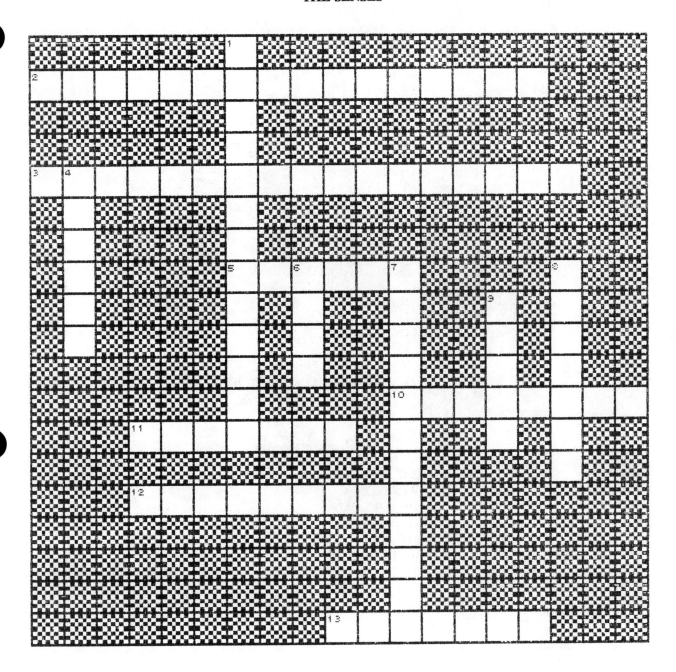

ACROSS

2. Eardrum (2 words)
3. Receptors for balance in semicircular canals (2 words)
5. White of the eye
10. Bones of the middle ear
11. Front part of this coat is the ciliary muscle and iris
12. Membranous labyrinth filled with this fluid
13. External ear

DOWN

1. Located in posterior cavity
4. Innermost layer of eye
6. Transparent body behind pupil
7. Located in anterior cavity in front of lens (2 words)
8. Organ of Corti located here
9. Hole in center of iris

EYE

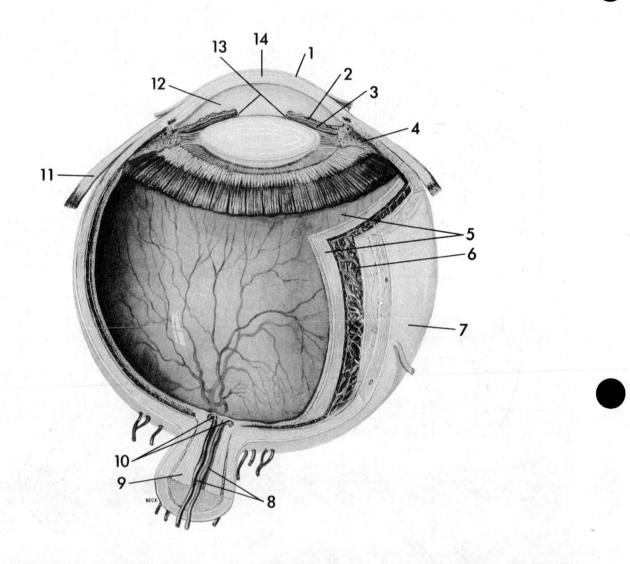

1. _CONJUNCTIVA_ X
2. _IRIS_ ✓
3. _POSTERIOR CAVITY_ X
4. _CILIARY MUSCLE_ ✓
5. _RETINA_ ✓
6. _CHOROID_ ✓
7. _SCLERA_ ✓
8. _CENTRAL RETINAL ARTERY + VEIN_ X
9. _OPTIC NERVE_ ✓
10. _OPTIC DISC (BLIND SPOT)_
11. _MUSCLE (MEDIAL RECTUS MUS)_ ½
12. _ANTERIOR CAVITY_ ✓
13. _PUPIL_ ✓
14. _CORNEA_

EAR

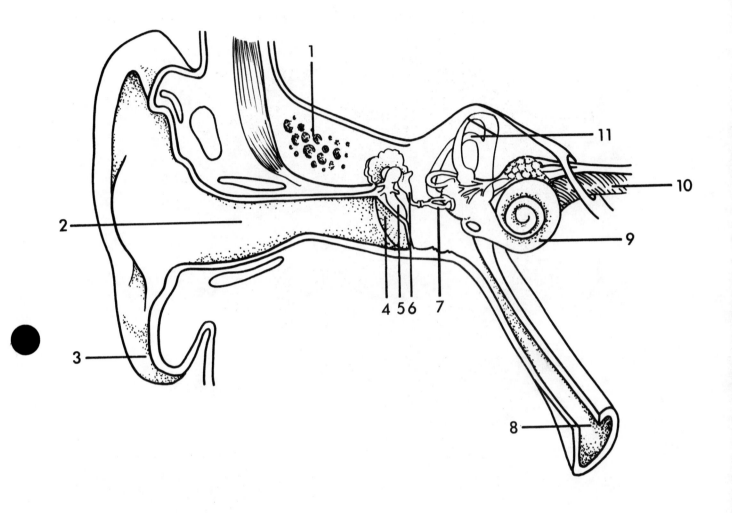

1. _____   7. _____

2. _____   8. _____

3. _____   9. _____

4. _____   10. _____

5. _____   11. _____

6. _____

CHAPTER 10

The Endocrine System

The endocrine system has often been compared to a fine concert symphony. When all instruments are playing properly, the sound is melodious. If one instrument plays too loud or too soft, however, it affects the overall quality of the entire performance.

The endocrine system is a ductless system that releases hormones into the bloodstream to help regulate body functions. The pituitary gland may be considered the conductor of the orchestra, as it stimulates many of the endocrine glands to secrete their powerful hormones. All hormones, whether stimulated in this manner or by other control mechanisms, are interdependent. A change in the level of one hormone may affect the level of many other hormones.

In addition to the endocrine glands, prostaglandins, or "tissue hormones," are powerful substances similar to hormones that have been found in a variety of body tissues. These hormones are often produced in a tissue and diffuse only a short distance to act on cells within that area. Prostaglandins influence respiration, blood pressure, gastrointestinal secretions, and the reproductive system and may some day play an important role in the treatment of diseases such as hypertension, asthma, and ulcers.

The endocrine system is a system of communication and control. It differs from the nervous system in that hormones provide a slower, longer lasting effect than do nerve stimuli and responses. Your understanding of the "system of hormones" will alert you to the mechanism of our emotions, response to stress, growth, chemical balances, and many other body functions.

TOPICS FOR REVIEW

Before progressing to Chapter 11, you should be able to identify and locate the primary endocrine glands of the body. Your understanding should include the hormones that are produced by these glands and the method by which these secretions are regulated. Your study will conclude with the pathological conditions that result from the malfunctioning of this system.

MECHANISMS OF HORMONE ACTION
REGULATION OF HORMONE SECRETION
MECHANISMS OF ENDOCRINE DISEASE
PROSTAGLANDINS

Match the term on the left with the proper selection on the right.

Group A

_____ 1. Pituitary		a. Pelvic cavity
_____ 2. Parathyroids		b. Mediastinum
_____ 3. Adrenals		c. Neck
_____ 4. Ovaries		d. Cranial cavity
_____ 5. Thymus		e. Abdominal cavity

_____ 6. Negative feedback
_____ 7. Tissue hormones
_____ 8. Second messenger hypothesis
_____ 9. Exocrine glands
_____ 10. Target organ cells

a. Explanation for hormone organ recognition
b. Respond to a particular hormone
c. Prostaglandins
d. Discharge secretions into ducts
e. Specialized homeostatic mechanism that regulates release of hormones

Fill in the blanks.

The (11) _____ _____ hypothesis is a theory that attempts to explain why hormones

cause specific effects in target organs but do not (12) _____ or act on other organs of the body.

Hormones serve as (13) _____ _____, providing communication between endocrine

glands and (14) _____ _____. The second messenger (15)

_____ provides communication within a hormone's (16) _____ _____.

(17) _____ _____ disrupts the normal negative feedback control of hormones

throughout the body, and may result in tissue damage, sterility, mental imbalance, and a host of life-threatening

metabolic problems.

▶ If you have had difficulty with this section, review pages 258-264. ◀

PITUITARY GLAND
HYPOTHALAMUS

Circle the correct choice.

18. The pituitary gland lies in the _____ bone.

    a. Ethmoid
    b. Sphenoid
    c. Temporal

    d. Frontal
    e. Occipital

19. Which one of the following structures would *not* be stimulated by a trophic hormone from the anterior pituitary?

    a. Ovaries
    b. Testes
    c. Thyroid

    d. Adrenals
    e. Uterus

20. Which one of the following is *not* a function of FSH?

    a. Stimulates the growth of follicles
    b. Stimulates the production of estrogens
    c. Stimulates the growth of seminiferous tubules
    d. Stimulates the interstitial cells of the testes

21. Which one of the following is *not* a function of LH?

    a. Stimulates maturation of a developing follicle
    b. Stimulates the production of estrogens
    c. Stimulates the formation of a corpus luteum
    d. Stimulates sperm cells to mature in the male
    e. Causes ovulation to occur

22. Which one of the following is *not* a function of GH?

    a. Increases glucose catabolism
    b. Increases fat catabolism
    c. Speeds up the movement of amino acids into cells from the bloodstream.
    d. All of the above are functions of GH

23. Which one of the following hormones is *not* released by the anterior pituitary gland?

    a. ACTH   d. FSH
    b. TSH   e. LH
    c. ADH

24. Which one of the following is *not* a function of prolactin?

    a. Stimulates breast development during pregnancy
    b. Stimulates milk secretion after delivery
    c. Causes the release of milk from glandular cells of the breast
    d. All of the above are functions of prolactin

25. The anterior pituitary gland:

    a. Secretes eight major hormones
    b. Secretes trophic hormones that stimulate other endocrine glands to grow and secrete
    c. Secretes ADH
    d. Secretes oxytocin

26. TSH acts on the:

    a. Thyroid   c. Pineal
    b. Thymus   d. Testes

27. ACTH stimulates the:

    a. Adrenal cortex   c. Hypothalamus
    b. Adrenal medulla   d. Ovaries

28. Which hormone is secreted by the posterior pituitary gland?

   a. MSH
   b. LH

   c. GH
   d. ADH

29. ADH serves the body by:

   a. Initiating labor
   b. Accelerating water reabsorption from urine into the blood
   c. Stimulating the pineal gland
   d. Regulating the calcium/phosphorus levels in the blood

30. The disease caused by hyposecretion of the ADH is:

   a. Diabetes insipidus
   b. Diabetes mellitus

   c. Acromegaly
   d. Myxedema

31. The actual production of ADH and oxytocin takes place in which area?

   a. Anterior pituitary
   b. Posterior pituitary

   c. Hypothalamus
   d. Pineal

32. Inhibiting hormones are produced by the:

   a. Anterior pituitary
   b. Posterior pituitary

   c. Hypothalamus
   d. Pineal

Select the best answer from the choices given and insert the letter in the answer blank.

(a) Anterior pituitary   (b) Posterior pituitary   (c) Hypothalamus

_____33. Adenohypophysis
_____34. Neurohypophysis
_____35. Induced labor
_____36. Appetite
_____37. Acromegaly
_____38. Body temperature
_____39. Sex hormones
_____40. Trophic hormones
_____41. Gigantism
_____42. Releasing hormones

▶ If you have had difficulty with this section, review pages 265-268. ◀

THYROID GLAND
PARATHYROID GLANDS

Circle the correct answer.

43. The thyroid gland lies (above or below) the larynx.

44. The thyroid gland secretes (calcitonin or glucagon).

45. For thyroxine to be produced in adequate amounts, the diet must contain sufficient (calcium or iodine).

46. Most endocrine glands (do or do not) store their hormones.

47. Colloid is a storage medium for the (thyroid hormone or parathyroid hormone).

48. Calcitonin (increases or decreases) the concentration of calcium in the blood.

49. Simple goiter results from (hyperthyroidism or hypothyroidism).

50. Hyposecretion of thyroid hormones during the formative years leads to (cretinism or myxedema).

51. The parathyroid glands secrete the hormone (PTH or PTA).

52. Parathyroid hormone tends to (increase or decrease) the concentration of calcium in the blood.

▸ If you have had difficulty with this section, review pages 268-271. ◂

ADRENAL GLANDS

Fill in the blanks.

53. The adrenal gland is actually two separate endocrine glands, the _____ _____ and the

_____ _____.

54. Hormones secreted by the adrenal cortex are known as _____.

55. The outer zone of the adrenal cortex, the zona glomerulosa, secretes _____.

56. The middle zone, the zona fasciculata, secretes _____.

57. The innermost zone, the zona reticularis, secretes _____.

58. Glucocorticoids act in several ways to increase _____.

59. Glucocorticoids also play an essential part in maintaining _____ _____.

60. The adrenal medulla secretes the hormones _____ and _____.

61. The adrenal medulla may help the body resist _____.

62. The term _____ _____ _____ is often used to describe how the body mobilizes a number of different defense mechanisms when threatened by harmful stimuli.

Select the best response from the choices given and insert the letter in the answer blank.

(a) Adrenal cortex   (b) Adrenal medulla

____ 63. Addison's disease
____ 64. Anti-immunity
____ 65. Adrenaline

_____66. Cushing's syndrome
_____67. Fight or flight syndrome
_____68. Aldosterone
_____69. Androgens

▸ If you have had difficulty with this section, review pages 261-276. ◂

PANCREATIC ISLETS
SEX GLANDS
THYMUS
PLACENTA
PINEAL GLAND

Circle the term that does not belong.

70. Alpha cells	Glucagon	Beta cells	Glycogenolysis
71. Insulin	Glucagon	Beta cells	Diabetes mellitus
72. Estrogens	Progesterone	Corpus luteum	Thymosin
73. Chorion	Interstitial cells	Testosterone	Semen
74. Immune system	Mediastinum	Aldosterone	Thymosin
75. Pregnancy	ACTH	Estrogen	Chorion
76. Melatonin	Menstruation	"Third eye"	Semen

APPLYING WHAT YOU KNOW

77. Mrs. Fortner made a routine visit to her physician last week. When the laboratory results came back, the report indicated a high level of chorionic gonadotropin in her urine. What did this mean to Mrs. Fortner?

78. Mrs. Calhoun noticed that her daughter was beginning to take on the secondary sex characteristics of a male. The pediatrician diagnosed the condition as a tumor of an endocrine gland. Where specifically was the tumor located?

79. WORD FIND

Can you find the terms from the chapter listed below in the box of letters? Words may be spelled top to bottom, bottom to top, right to left, left to right, or diagonally.

```
J C W W H Y P E R C A L C E M I A L E D
T P Y E S K A A R T E S Y E Z S G Z Z E
B O U D D O M L E T X D J N I Y D B P O
L F Y X D E S W T G W I R O F A G D M S
N H S S D Q P F I U P A G M U V E Q G Z
O Q Z E Q N U A O I M B B R T J F M W M
P V X U V F O D G Z A E K O L O R Y G V
R Y G R Z O H G X T O T G H V K E D T E
M J I O I X D J A A N E D E F D N J Q H
N V J Q V M H Y Y C O S C Q I N D Z P Y
C R E T I N I S M Q U L P U N L O I B P
E X O C R I N E Z Z M L R K N R C Y S O
V D A R I B T J V P C E G L C U R F I G
S E H R I T Q O K J S F G W Q K I T M L
R C O H J F R Q S I M F D I X P N L E Y
X R O M T L L P S U E B X D E M E T O C
M F S D I O C I T R O C N Z P O Q K J E
M S T R E S S S D I O R E T S M T A M M
U P P U N O I T A Z I N I E T U L H V I
U P R O S T A G L A N D I N S C E A C A
```

LIST OF WORDS

CORTICOIDS
DIURESIS
GOITER
HYPOGLYCEMIA
MYXEDEMA
GLUCAGON

CRETINISM
ENDOCRINE
HORMONE
LUTEINIZATION
PROSTAGLANDINS

DIABETES
EXOCRINE
HYPERCALCEMIA
STEROIDS
STRESS

DID YOU KNOW?

The total daily output of the pituitary gland is less than 1/1,000,000 of a gram.

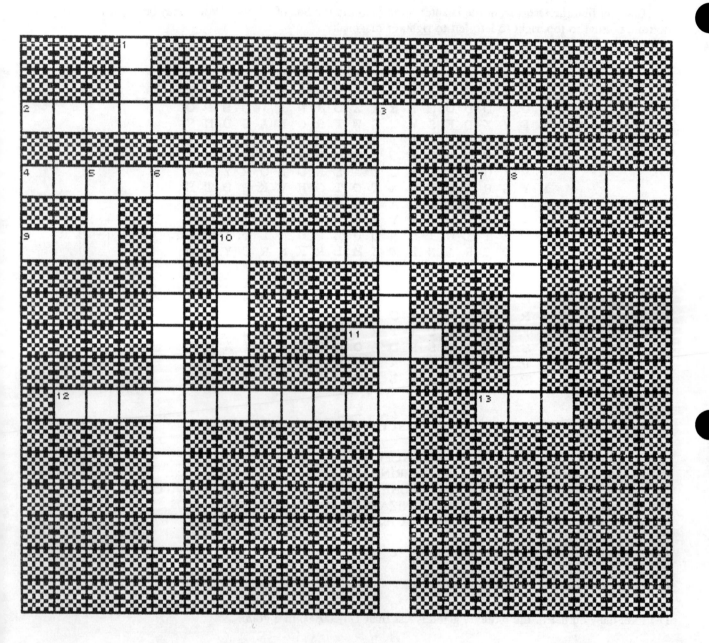

ACROSS

2. Hypersecretion of glucocorticoids
4. Hypersecretion of insulin
7. Hyposecretion of thyroid
9. Antagonist to diuresis
10. Hypersecretion of growth hormone
11. Estrogens
12. Adrenal medulla
13. Secreted by cells in the walls of the heart's atria

DOWN

1. Melanin
3. Hyposecretion of Islands of Langerhans (2 words)
5. Increases calcium concentration
6. Converts amino acids to glucose
8. Labor
10. Adrenal cortex

ENDOCRINE GLANDS

1. _____

2. _____

3. _____

4. _____

5. _____

6. _____

7. _____

8. _____

9. _____

CHAPTER 11

Blood

Blood, the river of life, is the body's primary means of transportation. Although it is the respiratory system that provides oxygen for the body, the digestive system that provides nutrients, and the urinary system that eliminates wastes, none of these functions could be provided for the individual cells without the blood. In less than one minute, a drop of blood will complete a trip through the entire body, distributing nutrients and collecting the wastes of metabolism.

Blood is divided into plasma, which is the liquid portion of blood, and the formed elements, which are the blood cells. There are three types of blood cells: red blood cells, white blood cells, and platelets. Together these cells and plasma provide a means of transportation that delivers the body's daily necessities.

Although the red blood cells in all of us are of a similar shape, we have different blood types. Blood types are identified by the presence of certain antigens in the red blood cells. Every person's blood belongs to one of four main blood groups: Type A, B, AB, or O. Any one of the four groups or "types" may or may not have the Rh factor present in the red blood cells. If an individual has a specific antigen called the Rh factor present in his or her blood, the blood is Rh positive. If this factor is missing, the blood is Rh negative. Approximately, 85% of the population have the Rh factor (Rh positive) while 15% do not have the Rh factor (Rh negative).

Your understanding of this chapter will be necessary to prepare a proper foundation for the circulatory system.

TOPICS FOR REVIEW

Before progressing to Chapter 12, you should have an understanding of the structure and function of blood plasma and cells. Your review should also include a knowledge of blood types and Rh factors.

BLOOD COMPOSITION

Circle the best answer.

1. Another name for white blood cells is:

    a. Erythrocytes
    b. Leukocytes

    c. Thrombocytes
    d. Platelets

2. Another name for platelets is:

    a. Neutrophils
    b. Eosinophils

    c. Thrombocytes
    d. Erythrocytes

3. Pernicious anemia is caused by:

    a. A lack of vitamin B_{12}
    b. Hemorrhage

    c. Radiation
    d. Bleeding ulcers

4. The laboratory test called hematocrit tells the physician:

   a. The volume of white cells in a blood sample
   b. The volume of red cells in a blood sample
   c. The volume of platelets in a blood sample
   d. The volume of plasma in a blood sample

5. An example of a nongranular leukocyte is a/an:

   a. Platelet
   b. Erythrocyte

   c. Eosinophil
   d. Monocyte

6. An abnormally high white blood cell count is known as:

   a. Leukemia
   b. Leukopenia

   c. Leukocytosis
   d. Anemia

7. A critical component of hemoglobin is:

   a. Potassium
   b. Calcium

   c. Vitamin K
   d. Iron

8. Sickle cell anemia is caused by:

   a. The production of an abnormal type of hemoglobin
   b. The production of excessive neutrophils
   c. The production of excessive platelets
   d. The production of abnormal leukocytes

9. The practice of using blood transfusions to increase oxygen delivery to muscles during athletic events is called:

   a. Blood antigen
   b. Blood doping

   c. Blood agglutination
   d. Blood proofing

10. The term used to describe the condition of a circulating blood clot is:

    a. Thrombosis
    b. Embolism

    c. Hemoglobin
    d. Platelet

11. Which one of the following types of cells is *not* a granular leukocyte?

    a. Neutrophil
    b. Monocyte

    c. Basophil
    d. Eosinophil

12. If a blood cell has no nucleus and is shaped like a biconcave disc, then the cell most likely is a/an:

    a. Platelet
    b. Lymphocyte
    c. Basophil

    d. Eosinophil
    e. Red blood cell

13. Red bone marrow forms all kinds of blood cells except:

    a. Platelets and basophils
    b. Lymphocytes and monocytes
    c. Red blood cells
    d. Neutrophils and eosinophils

14. Myeloid tissue is found in all but which one of the following locations?

    a. Sternum
    b. Ribs
    c. Wrist bones
    d. Hip bones
    e. Cranial bones

15. Lymphatic tissue is found in all but which of the following locations?

    a. Lymph nodes
    b. Thymus
    c. Spleen
    d. All of the above contain lymphatic tissue

16. The "buffy coat" layer in a hematocrit tube contains:

    a. Red blood cells
    b. Plasma
    c. Platelets
    d. White blood cells
    e. Two of the above are correct

17. The hematocrit value for red blood cells is _____%.

    a. 75
    b. 60
    c. 50
    d. 45
    e. 35

18. An unusually low white blood cell count would be termed:

    a. Leukemia
    b. Leukopenia
    c. Leukocytosis
    d. Anemia
    e. None of the above is correct

19. Most of the oxygen transported in the blood is carried by:

    a. Platelets
    b. Plasma
    c. White blood cells
    d. Red blood cells
    e. None of the above is correct

20. The most numerous of the phagocytes are the _____.

    a. Lymphocytes
    b. Neutrophils
    c. Basophils
    d. Eosinophils
    e. Monocytes

21. Which one of the following types of cells is *not* phagocytic?

    a. Neutrophils
    b. Eosinophils
    c. Lymphocytes
    d. Monocytes
    e. All of the above are phagocytic cells

22. Which of the following cell types functions in the immune process?

a. Neutrophils
b. Lymphocytes
c. Monocytes

d. Basophils
e. Reticuloendothelial cells

23. The organ that manufactures prothrombin is the:

a. Liver
b. Pancreas
c. Thymus

d. Kidney
e. Spleen

24. Which one of the following vitamins acts to accelerate blood clotting?

a. A
b. B
c. C

d. D
e. K

25. Which one of the following substances is *not* a part of the plasma?

a. Hormones
b. Salts
c. Nutrients

d. Wastes
e. All of the above are part of the plasma

26. The normal volume of blood in an adult is about:

a. 2-3 pints
b. 2-3 quarts

c. 2-3 gallons
d. 4-6 liters

27. Blood is normally:

a. Very acidic
b. Slightly acidic

c. Neutral
d. Slightly alkaline

28. This disease usually occurs as a result of the destruction of bone marrow by toxic chemicals or radiation.

a. Folate-deficiency anemia
b. Aplastic anemia

c. Hemolytic anemia
d. Sickle cell anemia

29. An example of a hemolytic anemia is:

a. Folate-deficiency anemia
b. Aplastic anemia

c. Sickle cell anemia
d. Pernicious anemia

30. The disease that results from a failure to form blood clotting factor VIII, IX, or XI is:

a. Hemophilia
b. Thrombocytopenia

c. Thrombophlebitis
d. None of the above

31. An enzyme found in high concentration after massive tissue damage is:

a. Prothrombin
b. Alkaline phosphatase

c. Transaminase
d. None of the above

► If you have had difficulty with this section, review pages 288-298. ◄

BLOOD TYPES
RH FACTOR

Fill in the blank areas.

32.

Blood Type	Antigen Present in RBC	Antibody Present in Plasma
A		Anti-B
B	B	
AB		None
O	None	

Fill in the blanks

33. An _____ is a substance that can stimulate the blood to make antibodies.

34. An _____ is a substance made by the body in response to stimulation by an antigen.

35. Many antibodies react with their antigens to clump or _____ them.

36. If a baby is born to an Rh-negative mother and Rh-positive father, it may develop the disease _____ _____.

37. The term "Rh" is used because the antigen was first discovered in the blood of a _____ _____.

38. The universal donor blood is _____.

39. The universal recipient blood is _____.

► If you have had difficulty with this section, review pages 298-301. ◄

APPLYING WHAT YOU KNOW

40. Mrs. Payne's blood type is O positive. Her husband's type is O negative. Her newborn baby's blood type is O negative. Is there any need for concern with this combination?

115

41. After Mrs. Freund's baby was born, the doctor applied a gauze dressing for a short time on the umbilical cord. He also gave the baby a dose of vitamin K. Why did the doctor perform these two procedures?

42. **WORD FIND**

Can you find the terms from this chapter listed below in the box of letters? Words may be spelled top to bottom, bottom to top, right to left, left to right, or diagonally.

```
I T C S U B M O R H T E L Z F Q I H T Q
X W R Y B H E Y P H A G O C Y T E S L N
G Q E K A E M X M L T R P I N J X V E H
L V C Q S M B R N M T H R O M B I N U V
E W I L O O O U A Q K O H T S U M I K S
U O P N P G L Q P Q R Y X E S O H S E Z
K M I M H L U C A O M X T F N B W R M V
O G E D I O S O I Y P Y A O R G S J I Z
C S N N L B J I D Q C C C X Z J I E A H
Y U T M P I L V S O T Y F J W E J Q U S
T S T R O N O D R O T N A E O A E B C W
E E X P B Z F H R E Y N T V W E U S M I
S H N V K G T D H H T A F G Q M B I A T
S R I M J Y L T T I X N A M S A L P Y T
F R R T R W O C G I G T I E P Y T A B S
U Q B E I P L E V S N I B C L Y U E E R
V T I B S I N R X W O B X Y C K E R R C
E Z F E N A I M E N A O J S E K U X H S
N I R A P E H O X Z I D P M Z M F D Z Q
H E M A T O C R I T R Y Z I P N C L G W
```

LIST OF WORDS

PLASMA	ERYTHROCYTES	LEUKOCYTES
ANEMIA	HEMOGLOBIN	HEMATOCRIT
AIDS	LEUKEMIA	PHAGOCYTES
MONOCYTE	THROMBUS	FIBRIN
HEPARIN	EMBOLUS	SERUM
FACTOR	TYPE	ANTIBODY
ANTIGEN	THROMBIN	BASOPHIL
DONOR	RECIPIENT	RHESUS

DID YOU KNOW?

Every pound of excess fat contains some 200 miles of additional capillaries to push blood through.

116

BLOOD

ACROSS

1. Abnormally high WBC count
4. Final stage of clotting process
5. Substances that stimulate the body to make antibodies
7. Platelets
8. To engulf and digest microbes
11. RBC
12. Liquid portion of blood
13. Stationary blood clot

DOWN

2. Type O (two words)
3. Type of leukocyte
5. Inability of the blood to carry sufficient O2
6. Circulating blood clot
9. O2 carrying mechanism of blood
10. Prevents clotting of blood

HUMAN BLOOD CELLS

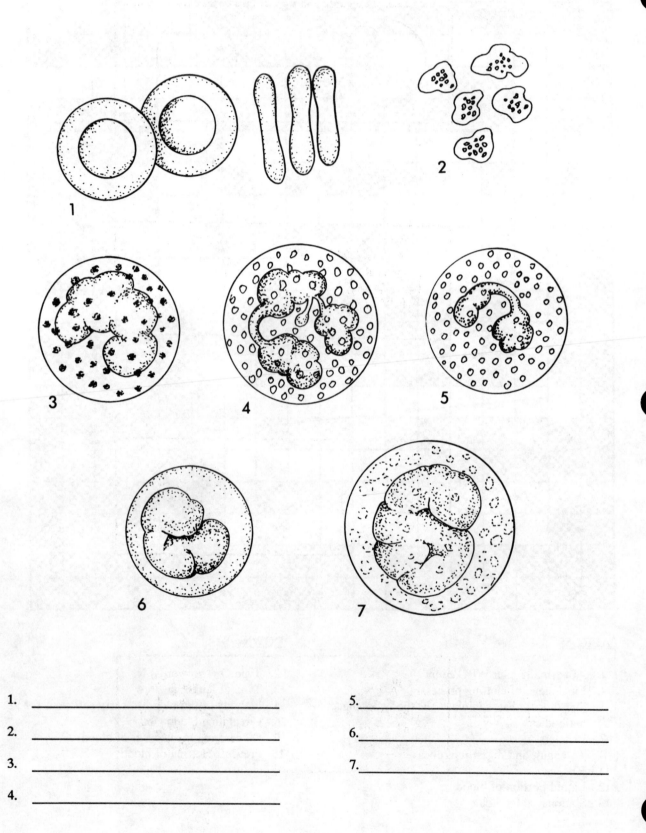

1. _____

2. _____

3. _____

4. _____

5. _____

6. _____

7. _____

BLOOD TYPING

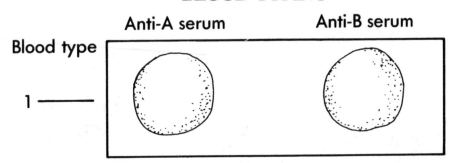

Anti-A serum | Anti-B serum

Blood type

1

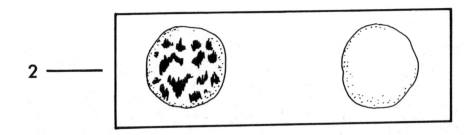

2

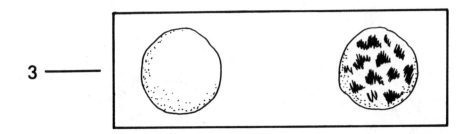

3

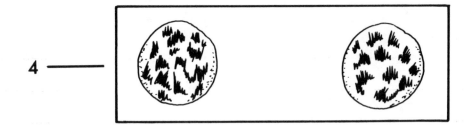

4

Normal blood

Agglutinated blood

119

CHAPTER 12

The Heart and Heart Disease

The heart is actually two pumps, one to move blood to the lungs, the other to push it out into the body. These two functions seem rather elementary by comparison to the complex and numerous functions performed by most of the other body organs, and yet, if this pump stops, within a few short minutes all life ceases.

The heart is divided into two upper compartments called atria or receiving chambers and two lower compartments or discharging chambers called ventricles. By age 45, approximately 300,000 tons of blood will have passed through these chambers to be circulated to the blood vessels. This closed system of circulation provides distribution of blood to the whole body (systemic circulation) and to specific regions, such as pulmonary circulation or coronary circulation.

The beating of the heart must be coordinated in a rhythmic manner if the heart if to pump effectively. This is achieved by electrical impulses which are stimulated by specialized structures embedded in the walls of the heart. The Sinoatrial node, Atrioventricular node, Bundle of HIS, and Purkinje fibers combine efforts to produce the tiny electrical currents necessary to contract the heart. Any interruption or failure of this system may result in serious pathology or even death.

A healthy heart is necessary to pump sufficient blood throughout the body to nourish and oxygenate cells continuously. Your review of this chapter will provide you with an understanding of this vital organ necessary for survival.

TOPICS FOR REVIEW

Before progressing to Chapter 13 you should have an understanding of the structure and function of the heart. Your review should include a study of coronary circulation and the conduction system of the heart. Your study should conclude with an understanding of the major coronary diseases and disorders.

ANATOMY OF THE HEART

Fill in the blanks.

1. The system that supplies our cells' transportation needs is the _CARDIOVASCULAR SYSTEM_ (CIRCULATORY).

2. The _SEPTUM_ divides the heart into right and left sides between the atria.

3. The _ATRIA_ are the two upper chambers of the heart.

4. The _VENTRICLES_ are the two lower chambers of the heart.

5. The cardiac muscle tissue is referred to as the _MYOCARDIUM_.

6. Inflammation of the heart lining is _ENDOCARDITIS_.

7. The two AV valves are _BICUSPID_ and _TRICUSPID_.

8. The inner layer of the pericardium is called the _VISCERAL PERICARDIUM_.

9. The outer layer of pericardium is called _PARIETAL PERICARDIUM_.

10. If the pericardium becomes inflamed, a condition called _PERICARDITIS_ results.

11. The _SEMI LUNAR VALVES_ are located between the two ventricular chambers and the large arteries that carry blood away from the heart when contraction occurs.

12. A _MITRAL VALVE PROLAPSE_ is a condition caused when the flaps of this valve extend back into the left atrium, causing leaking of the valve.

13. _RHEUMATIC HEART DISEASE_ is cardiac damage resulting from a delayed inflammatory response to streptococcal infection that occurs most often in children.

▸ If you have had difficulty with this section, review pages 308-313. ◂

HEART SOUNDS
BLOOD FLOW THROUGH THE HEART
CORONARY CIRCULATION AND CORONARY HEART DISEASE
HEART FAILURE

Select the best answer.

a. Heart murmur
b. Pulmonary circulation
c. Embolism
d. Heart attack
e. Angina pectoris

f. Systemic circulation
g. Atherosclerosis
h. Hypertension
i. Coronary bypass
j. Pulmonary veins

____F__ 14. Movement of blood from the left ventricle through the body
____C__ 15. Blood clot
____D__ 16. Myocardial infarction
____A__ 17. Abnormal heart sound often caused by disorders of the valves
____B__ 18. Movements of blood from the right ventricle to the lungs
____G__ 19. Hardening of the arteries
____E__ 20. Severe chest pain
____H__ 21. High blood pressure
____J__ 22. Blood returns to the left atrium through these structures
____I__ 23. Treatment for certain coronary disorders

CARDIAC CYCLE
CONDUCTION SYSTEM OF THE HEART

Circle the best answer.

24. The heart beats at an average rate of ____72____ beats per minute.

   a. 50
   b. 72

   c. 100
   d. 120

25. Decreased cardiac output can be caused by:

    a. Valve disorders
    b. Coronary artery blockage
    c. Myocardial infarction
    d. All of the above

26. The pacemaker of the heart is also known as the:

    a. SA node
    b. AV node
    c. AV bundle
    d. Purkinje fibers

27. A rapid heart rhythm, over 100 beats per minutes, is referred to as:

    a. Bradycardia
    b. Sinus arrhythmia
    c. Tachycardia
    d. Premature contractions

28. The term _____ describes the electrical activity that triggers contraction of the heart muscle.

    a. Depolarization
    b. Repolarization
    c. AV node block
    d. Cardiac arrhythmia

29. A diagnostic tool that uses ultrasound to detect valve and heart disorders is known as a/an:

    a. Electrocardiogram
    b. Pacemaker
    c. TPA
    d. Echocardiogram

30. Frequent premature contractions can lead to:

    a. Extrasystoles
    b. Bradycardia
    c. Fibrillation
    d. Heart failure

31. A drug that slows and increases the strength of cardiac contractions is:

    a. Digitalis
    b. Nitroglycerin
    c. Calcium-channel blocker
    d. Anticoagulant

32. Congestive heart failure inevitably causes:

    a. Extra systole
    b. Pulmonary edema
    c. Fibrillation
    d. Bradycardia

33. Failure to the right side of the heart due to blockage of pulmonary blood flow is called:

    a. Cardiomyopathy
    b. Ventricular fibrillation
    c. Cor pulmonale
    d. TPA

34. The Jarvik-7 is a/an:

    a. Artificial hart
    b. Beta-blocker
    c. Demand pacemaker
    d. ECG

35. Coumaden and Dicumarol are examples of commonly used oral:

    a. Beta-blockers
    b. Nitroglycerin
    c. Calcium-channel blockers
    d. Anticoagulants

▸ If you have had difficulty with this section review pages 313-322. ◂

APPLYING WHAT YOU KNOW

36. Else was experiencing angina pectoris. Her doctor suggested a surgical procedure that would require the removal of a vein from another region of her body. They would then use the vein to bypass a partial blockage in her coronary arteries. What is this procedure called? *Coronary Bypass*

37. Mrs. Frank has heart block. Her electrical impulses are being blocked from reaching the ventricles. An electrical device that causes ventricular contractions at a rate necessary to maintain circulation is being considered as possible treatment for her condition. What is this device? *Artificial Pacemaker*

38. Mrs. Calhoun was diagnosed with an acute case of endocarditis. What is the real danger of this diagnosis? *The endocardial lining can become rough and abrasive to red blood cells passing over its surface. As a result a fatal blood clot may be formed.*

DID YOU KNOW?

Your heart pumps more than 5 quarts of blood every minute or 2,000 gallons a day.

CIRCULATORY SYSTEM

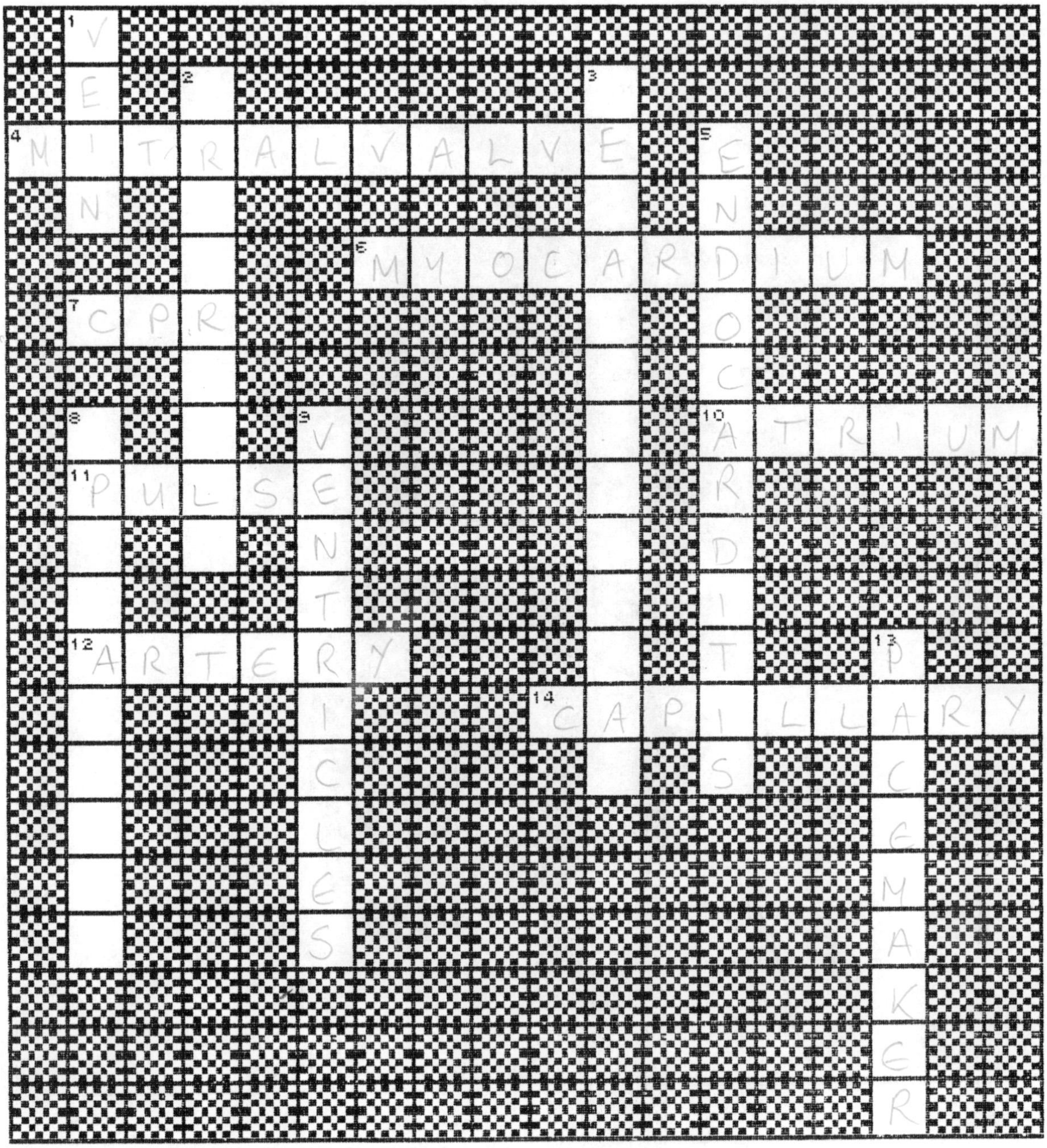
1 VEIN
2
3
4 MITRALVALVE
5 ENDOCARDITIS
6 MYOCARDIUM
7 CPR
8
9 VENTRICLES
10 ATRIUM
11 PULSE
12 ARTERY
13 PACEMAKER
14 CAPILLARY

ACROSS

4. Bicuspid valve (2 words)
6. Muscular layer of heart
7. Cardiopulmonary resuscitation (abbrev.)
10. Upper chamber of heart
11. Heart rate
12. Carries blood away from heart
14. Carries blood from arterioles into venules

DOWN

1. Carries blood to the heart
2. Tiny artery Arteriole
3. Unique blood circulation through the liver (2 words) Hepatic Portal
5. Inflammation of the lining of the heart
8. Inner layer of pericardium Epicardium
9. Lower chambers of the heart
13. SA node

THE HEART

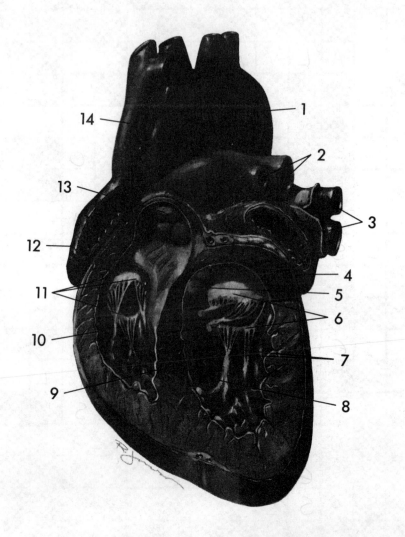

1. _____

2. _____

3. _____

4. _____

5. _____

6. _____

7. CHORDAE TENAE _____

8. _____

9. _____

10. _____

11. _____

12. _____

13. _____

14. _____

CONDUCTION SYSTEM OF THE HEART

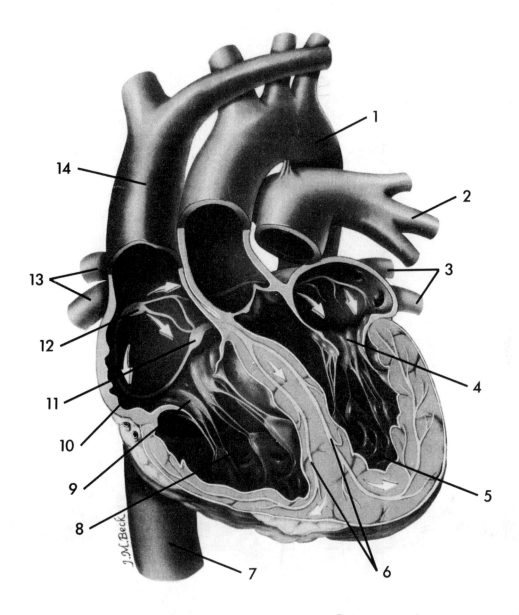

J.M.Beck

1. AORTA
2. PULMONARY ARTERY
3. PULMONARY VEINS
4. MITRAL VALVE
5. LEFT VENTRICLE
6. R+L BRANCHES OF AV BUNDLE
7. VENA CAVA (INFERIOR)

8. RIGHT VENTRICLE
9. TRICUSPID VALVE
10. RIGHT ATRIUM
11. ATRIOVENTRICULAR NODE
12. SINO ATRIAL NODE
13. PULMONARY VEINS
14. SUPERIOR VENA CAVA

127

NORMAL ECG DEFLECTIONS

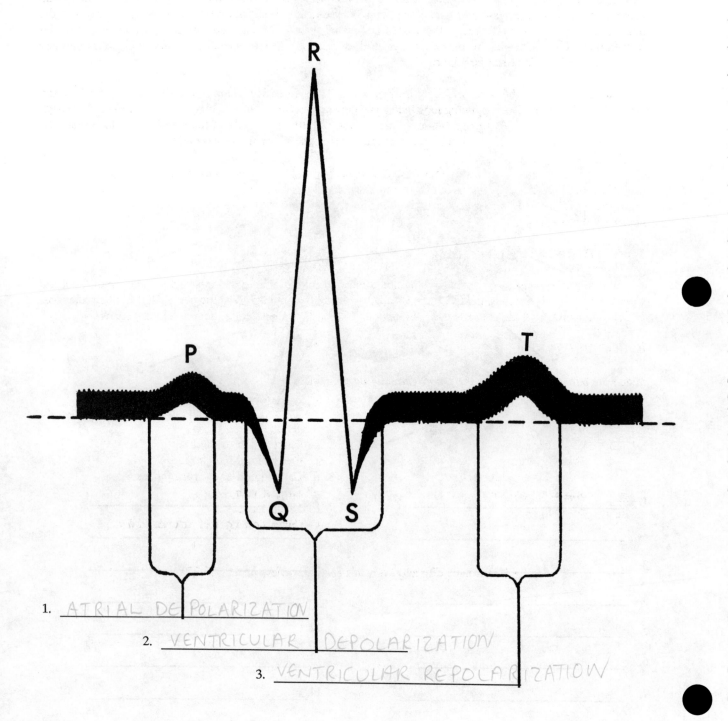

1. ATRIAL DEPOLARIZATION
2. VENTRICULAR DEPOLARIZATION
3. VENTRICULAR REPOLARIZATION

CHAPTER 13

Circulation of the Blood

One hundred thousand miles of blood vessels make up the elaborate transportation system that circulates materials for energy, growth and repair, and eliminates wastes for your body. These vessels, called arteries, veins, and capillaries serve different functions. Arteries carry blood from the heart, veins carry blood to the heart and capillaries are exchange vessels or connecting links between the arteries and veins. The pumping action of the heart keeps blood moving through the closed system of vessels. This closed system of circulation provides distribution of blood to the whole body (systemic circulation) and to specific regions, such as pulmonary circulation, or hepatic portal circulation.

Blood pressure is the force of blood in the vessels. This force is highest in arteries and lowest in veins. Normal blood pressure varies among individuals and depends on the volume of blood in the arteries. The larger the volume of blood in the arteries, the more pressure is exerted on the walls of the arteries, and the higher the arterial pressure. Conversely, the less blood in the arteries, the lower the blood pressure.

A functional cardiovascular system is vital for survival because without circulation, tissues would lack a supply of oxygen and nutrients. Waste products would begin to accumulate and could become toxic. Your review of this system will provide you with an understanding of the complex transportation mechanism of the body necessary for survival.

TOPICS FOR REVIEW

Before progressing to Chapter 14 you should have an understanding of the structure and function of the blood vessels. Your review should include a study of systemic, pulmonary, hepatic portal, and fetal circulations, and should conclude with a thorough understanding of blood pressure, pulse, and circulatory shock.

BLOOD VESSELS

Match the term on the left with the proper selection on the right.

_____	1.	Arteries	a. Smooth muscle cells that guard entrance to capillaries
_____	2.	Veins	b. Carry blood to the heart
_____	3.	Capillaries	c. Carry blood into venules
_____	4.	Tunica externa	d. Carry blood away from the heart
_____	5.	Precapillary sphincters	e. Largest vein
_____	6.	Superior vena cava	f. Largest artery
_____	7.	Aorta	g. Outermost layer of arteries and veins

► If you have difficulty with this section, review pages 327-329. ◄

DISORDERS OF BLOOD VESSELS

a. Atherosclerosis
b. Ischemia
c. Aneurysm
d. Necrosis
e. Gangrene

f. Hemorrhoids
g. Phlebitis
h. Stroke
i. Arteriosclerosis
j. Thrombus

_____ 8. Hardening of the arteries
_____ 9. Decreased blood supply to a tissue
_____ 10. Tissue death
_____ 11. Necrosis that has progressed to decay
_____ 12. A type of arteriosclerosis caused by lipids
_____ 13. A section of an artery that has become abnormally widened
_____ 14. Varicose veins in the rectum
_____ 15. Vein inflammation
_____ 16. Clot formation
_____ 17. Cerebral vascular accident

▸ If you have had difficulty with this section, review pages 333-335. ◂

CIRCULATION OF BLOOD

Circle the best answer.

18. The aorta carries blood out of the:

    a. Right atrium
    b. Left atrium
    c. Right ventricle

    d. Left ventricle
    e. None of the above is correct

19. The superior vena cava returns blood to the:

    a. Left atrium
    b. Left ventricle
    c. Right atrium

    d. Right ventricle
    e. None of the above is correct

20. The _____ function as exchange vessels.

    a. Venules
    b. Capillaries
    c. Arteries

    d. Arterioles
    e. Veins

21. Blood returns from the lungs during pulmonary circulation via the:

    a. Pulmonary artery
    b. Pulmonary veins

    c. Aorta
    d. Inferior vena cava

22. The hepatic portal circulation serves the body by:

    a. Removing excess glucose and storing it in the liver as glycogen
    b. Detoxifying blood
    c. Removing various poisonous substances present in blood
    d. All of the above

23. The structure used to bypass the liver in fetal circulation is the:

    a. Foramen ovale
    b. Ductus venosus

    c. Ductus arteriosus
    d. Umbilical vein

24. The foramen ovale serves the fetal circulation by:

    a. Connecting the aorta and the pulmonary artery
    b. Shunting blood from the right atrium directly into the left atrium
    c. Bypassing the liver
    d. Bypassing the lungs

25. The structure used to connect the aorta and pulmonary artery in fetal circulation is the:

    a. Ductus arteriosus
    b. Ductus venosus

    c. Aorta
    d. Foramen ovale

26. Which of the following is *not* an artery?

    a. Femoral
    b. Popliteal

    c. Coronary
    d. Inferior vena cava

► If you have had difficulty with this section, review pages 332 and 335-339. ◄

BLOOD PRESSURE
PULSE

*Mark **T** if the answer is true. If the answer is false, circle the wrong word(s) and correct the statement by inserting the proper word(s) in the answer blank.*

_____ 27. Blood pressure is highest in the veins and lowest in the arteries.
_____ 28. The difference between two blood pressures is referred to as blood pressure deficit.
_____ 29. If the blood pressure in the arteries were to decrease so that it became equal to the average pressure in the arterioles, circulation would increase.
_____ 30. A stroke is often the result of low blood pressure.
_____ 31. Massive hemorrhage increases blood pressure.
_____ 32. Blood pressure is the volume of blood in the vessels.
_____ 33. Both the strength and the rate of heartbeat affect cardiac output and blood pressure.
_____ 34. The diameter of the arterioles helps to determine how much blood drains out of arteries into arterioles.
_____ 35. A stronger heartbeat tends to decrease blood pressure and a weaker heartbeat tends to increase it.
_____ 36. The systolic pressure is the pressure while the ventricles relax.
_____ 37. The diastolic pressure is the pressure while the ventricles contract.
_____ 38. A device called a sphygmomanometer is used to measure blood pressures in clinical situations.

_____ 39. Loud, tapping Korotkoff sounds suddenly begin when the cuff pressure measured by the mercury column equals the systolic pressure.

_____ 40. The venous blood pressure within the left atrium is called the central venous pressure.

_____ 41. The pulse is a vein expanding and then recoiling.

_____ 42. The radial artery is located at the wrist.

_____ 43. The common carotid artery is located in the neck along the front edge of the sternocleidomastoid muscle.

_____ 44. The artery located at the bend of the elbow and used for locating the pulse is the dorsalis pedis.

▸ If you have had difficulty with this section, review pages 336-343. ◂

CIRCULATORY SHOCK

Fill in the blanks.

45. Complications of septicemia may result in _____ _____.

46. _____ _____ results from any type of heart failure.

47. An acute type of allergic reaction called _____ results in _____ _____ _____.

48. _____ _____ results from widespread dilation of blood vessels caused by an imbalance in autonomic stimulation of smooth muscles in vessel walls.

49. Hypovolemia means "_____ _____ _____."

50. A type of septic shock that results from staphylococcal infections that begin in the vagina of menstruating women and spread to the blood is _____ _____ _____.

▸ If you have had difficulty with this section, review page 344. ◂

Unscramble the words.

51. STMESYCI

52. NULVEE

53. RYTREA

54. USLEP

Take the circled letters, unscramble them, and fill in the statement.

How Noah survived the flood.

55.

APPLY WHAT YOU KNOW

56. Mrs. Levin was enjoying a picnic lunch one day when a bee suddenly flew down and stung her. Within seconds Mrs. Levin began to experience difficulty with breathing, tachycardia, a decrease in blood pressure, and cyanosis. What is Mrs. Levin experiencing?

57. Terry was scheduled to undergo extensive surgery. Her surgeon, Dr. Berger, requested that two units of blood be available for Terry should she require them. What complication of surgery was Dr. Berger hoping to avoid?

58. Rochelle is a hair stylist and works long hours. Lately she has noticed that her feet are sore and edematous. What might be the cause of these symptoms? What advice could offer Rochelle some relief from these symptoms?

DID YOU KNOW?

Your heart pumps more than 5 quarts of blood every minute or 2,000 gallons a day.

FETAL CIRCULATION

1. _____
2. _____
3. _____
4. _____
5. _____
6. _____
7. _____
8. _____
9. _____
10. _____
11. _____
12. _____
13. _____
14. _____
15. _____
16. _____
17. _____
18. _____
19. _____
20. _____
21. _____
22. _____
23. _____
24. _____
25. _____
26. _____
27. _____
28. _____

HEPATIC PORTAL CIRCULATION

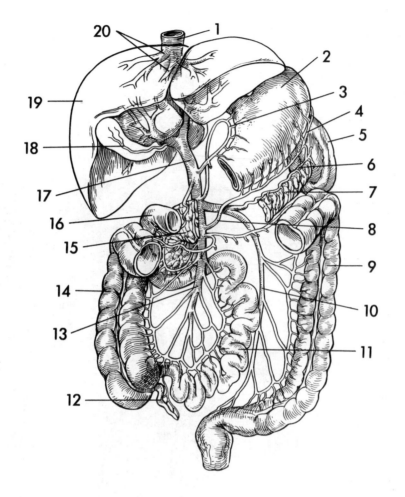

1. _____

2. _____

3. _____

4. _____

5. _____

6. _____

7. _____

8. _____

9. _____

10. _____

11. _____

12. _____

13. _____

14. _____

15. _____

16. _____

17. _____

18. _____

19. _____

20. _____

PRINCIPAL ARTERIES OF THE BODY

1. _____
2. _____
3. _____
4. _____
5. _____
6. _____
7. _____
8. _____
9. _____
10. _____
11. _____
12. _____
13. _____
14. _____
15. _____
16. _____
17. _____
18. _____
19. _____
20. _____
21. _____
22. _____
23. _____
24. _____
25. _____
26. _____
27. _____
28. _____
29. _____
30. _____

PRINCIPAL VEINS OF THE BODY

1. _____
2. _____
3. _____
4. _____
5. _____
6. _____
7. _____
8. _____
9. _____
10. _____
11. _____
12. _____
13. _____
14. _____
15. _____
16. _____
17. _____
18. _____
19. _____
20. _____
21. _____
22. _____
23. _____
24. _____
25. _____
26. _____
27. _____
28. _____
29. _____
30. _____
31. _____
32. _____
33. _____
34. _____

CHAPTER 14

The Lymphatic System and Immunity

The lymphatic system is a system similar to the circulatory system. Lymph, like blood, flows through an elaborate route of vessels. In addition to lymphatic vessels, the lymphatic system consists of lymph nodes, lymph, and the spleen. Unlike the circulatory system, the lymphatic vessels do not form a closed circuit. Lymph flows only once through the vessels before draining into the general blood circulation. This system is a filtering mechanism for microorganisms and serves as a protective device against foreign invaders, such as cancer.

The immune system is the armed forces division of the body. Ready to attack at a moments notice, the immune system defends us against the major enemies of the body: microorganisms, foreign transplanted tissue cells, and our own cells that have turned malignant.

The most numerous cells of the immune system are the lymphocytes. These cells circulate in the body's fluids seeking invading organisms and destroying them with powerful lymphotoxins, lymphokines, or antibodies.

Phagocytes, another large group of immune system cells, assist with the destruction of foreign invaders by a process known as phagocytosis. Neutrophils, monocytes, and connective tissue cells called macrophages use this process to surround unwanted microorganisms, ingest and digest them, rendering them harmless to the body.

Another weapon that the immune system possesses is complement. Normally a group of inactive enzymes present in the blood, complement can be activated to kill invading cells by drilling holes in their cytoplasmic membranes allowing fluid to enter the cell until it bursts.

Your review of this chapter will give you an understanding of how the body defends itself from the daily invasion of destructive substances.

TOPICS FOR REVIEW

Before progressing to Chapter 15 you should familiarize yourself with the functions of the lymphatic system, the immune system, and the major structures that make up these systems. Your review should include knowledge of lymphatic vessels, lymph nodes, lymph, antibodies, complement, and the development of B and T cells. Your study should also include the differences in humoral and cell-mediated immunity. Finally, an understanding of the excessive responses of the immune system and immune system deficiencies are necesary to complete your review of this chapter.

THE LYMPHATIC SYSTEM

Fill in the blanks.

1. _____ is a specialized fluid formed in the tissue spaces that will be transported by way of specialized vessels to eventually reenter the circulatory system.

2. Blood plasma that has filtered out of capillaries into microscopic spaces between cells is called _____.

3. The network of tiny blind-ended tubes distributed in the tissue spaces is called _____.

4. Lymph eventually empties into two terminal vessels called the _____ and the _____.

5. The thoracic duct has an enlarged pouchlike structure called the _____.

6. Lymph is filtered by moving through _____ which are located in clusters along the pathway of lymphatic vessels.

7. Lymph enters the node through four _____ lymph vessels.

8. Lymph exits from the node through a single _____ lymph vessel.

9. An abnormal condition in which tissues exhibit edema because of the accumulation of lymph is _____.

10. Hodgkin's disease is an example of _____.

► If you have had difficulty with this section, review pages 350-353. ◄

THYMUS
TONSILS
SPLEEN

Choose the correct response.

(a) Thymus   (b) Tonsils   (c) Spleen

_____11. Palatine, pharyngeal, and lingual are examples
_____12. Largest lymphoid organ in the body
_____13. Destroys worn out red blood cells
_____14. Located in the mediastinum
_____15. Serves as a reservoir for blood
_____16. T-lymphocytes
_____17. Largest at puberty

► If you have had difficulty with this section, review pages 353-354. ◄

THE IMMUNE SYSTEM

Match the term on the left with the proper selection on the right.

_____18. Nonspecific immunity   a. Inborn immunity
_____19. Inherited immunity   b. Natural immunity
_____20. Specific immunity   c. General protection
_____21. Acquired immunity   d. Artificial exposure
_____22. Immunization   e. Memory

IMMUNE SYSTEM MOLECULES

Choose the term that applies to each of the following descriptions. Place the letter for the term in the appropriate answer blank.

a. Antibodies
b. Antigen
c. Monoclonal
d. Complement fixation

e. Complement
f. Humoral
g. Combining site
h. Monocyte

_____23. Type of very specific antibodies produced from a population of identical cells
_____24. Protein compounds normally present in the body
_____25. Also known as antibody-mediated immunity
_____26. Combines with antibody to produce humoral immunity
_____27. Antibody
_____28. Process of changing molecule shape slightly to expose binding sites
_____29. Phagocyte
_____30. Inactive proteins in blood

▶ If you have had difficulty with this section, review pages 355-359. ◀

IMMUNE SYSTEM CELLS

Circle the best answer.

31. The most numerous cells of the immune system are the:

    a. Monocytes
    b. Eosinophils
    c. Neutrophils

    d. Lymphocytes
    e. Complement

32. Which of the terms listed below occurs third in the immune process?

    a. Plasma cells
    b. Stem cells
    c. Antibodies

    d. Activated B cells
    e. Immature B cells

33. Which one of the terms listed below occurs last in the immune process?

    a. Plasma cells
    b. Stem cells
    c. Antibodies

    d. Activated B cells
    e. Immature B cells

34. Which one of the following is part of the cell membrane of B cells?

    a. Complement
    b. Antigens
    c. Antibodies

    d. Epitopes
    e. None of the above

35. Immature B cells have:

   a. Four types of defense mechanisms on their cell membrane
   b. Several kinds of defense mechanisms on their cell membrane
   c. One specific kind of defense mechanism on their cell membrane
   d. No defense mechanisms on their cell membrane

36. Development of an immature B cell depends on the B cell coming in contact with:

   a. Complement   d. Lymphokines
   b. Antibodies   e. Antigens
   c. Lymphotoxins

37. The kind of cell that produces large numbers of antibodies is the:

   a. B cell   d. Memory cell
   b. Stem cell   e. Plasma cell
   c. T cell

38. Just one of these short-lived cells that make antibodies can produce _____ of them per second.

   a. 20   c. 2,000
   b. 200   d. 20,000

39. Which of the following statements is *not* true of memory cells?

   a. They produce large numbers of antibodies
   b. They are found in lymph nodes
   c. They develop into plasma cells
   d. They can react with antigens
   e. All of the above are true of memory cells

40. T cell development begins in the:

   a. Lymph nodes   d. Spleen
   b. Liver   e. Thymus
   c. Pancreas

41. B cells function indirectly to produce:

   a. Humoral immunity   c. Lymphotoxins
   b. Cell-mediated immunity d. Lymphokines

42. T cells function to produce:

   a. Humoral immunity   c. Antibodies
   b. Cell-mediated immunity d. Memory cells

▶ If you have had difficulty with this section, review pages 360-362. ◀

HYPERSENSITIVITY OF THE IMMUNE SYSTEM

Circle the correct answer.

43. The term allergy is used to describe (hypersensitivity or hyposensitivity) of the immune system to relatively harmless environmental antigens.

44. Antigens that trigger an allergic response are often called (antibodies or allergens).

45. (Anaphylactic shock or urticaria) is a life-threatening condition.

46. A common autoimmune disease is (lupus or SCID).

47. Erythroblastosis fetalis is an example of (isoimmunity or autoimmunity).

48. The antigens most commonly involved in transplant rejection are called (SCIDs or HLAs).

▶ If you have had difficulty with this section, review pages 363-365. ◀

IMMUNE DEFICIENCY SYSTEM

Select the correct response.

(a) Congenital   (b) Acquired (after birth)

_____49. AIDS
_____50. SCID
_____51. Improper B cell development prior to birth
_____52. ARC
_____53. Genetic defect

▶ If you have had difficulty with this section, review page 366. ◀

Unscramble the words.

54. NTCMPEOLEM

55. MTMYIUNI

56. OENCLS

57. FNROERTENI

...and please, don't let me forget to remember!

Take the circled letters, unscramble them, and fill in the statement.

What the student was praying for the night before exams.

58.

APPLYING WHAT YOU KNOW

59. Two-year old baby Metcalfe was exposed to chickenpox and subsequently developed the disease. What type of immunity will be developed as a result of this?

60. Sam was a bisexual and an intravenous drug user. He has developed a type of skin cancer known as Kaposi's sarcoma. What is Sam's primary diagnosis?

61. Baby Coyle was born without a thymus gland. Immediate plans were made for a transplant to be performed. In the meantime, baby Coyle was placed in strict isolation. For what reason was he placed in isolation?

DID YOU KNOW?

In 1990 there were 1700 new cases of AIDS in women and 1100 new cases of AIDS in men that were transmitted heterosexually.

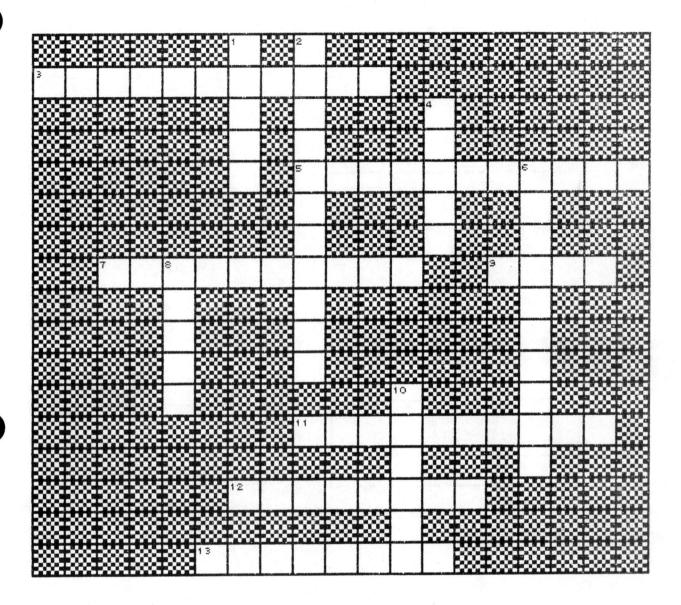

ACROSS

3. Remain in reserve then turn into plasma cells when needed (2 words)
5. Connective tissue cells that are phagocytes
7. Synthetically produced to fight certain diseases
9. Immune deficiency disorder
11. Inactive proteins
12. Lymph enters the node through these lymph vessels
13. Lymph exits the node through this lymph vessel

DOWN

1. Type of lymphocyte (humoral immunity—2 words)
2. Secretes a copious amount of antibodies into the blood (2 words)
4. Family of identical cells descended from one cell
6. Protein compounds normally present in the body
8. Type of lymphocyte (cell-mediated immunity—2 words)
10. Largest lymphoid organ in the body

B CELL DEVELOPMENT

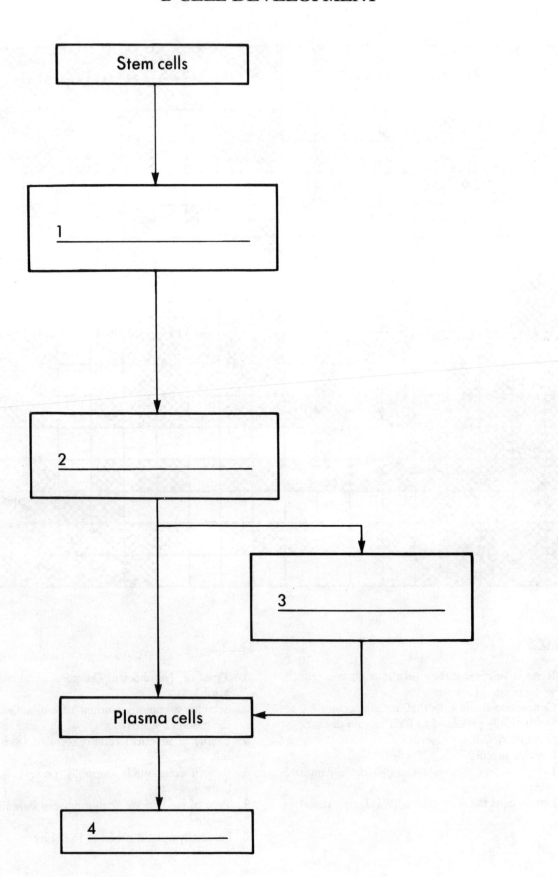

Stem cells

1 _____

2 _____

3 _____

Plasma cells

4 _____

FUNCTION OF SENSITIZED T CELLS

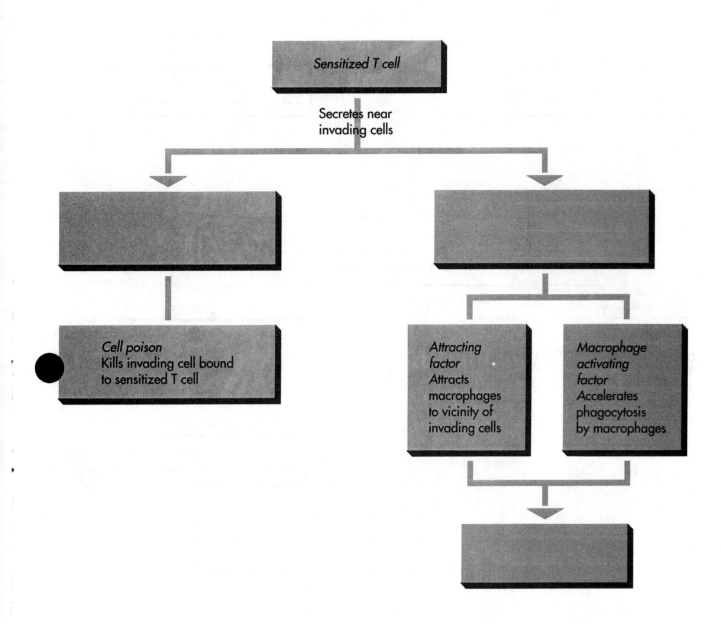

FUNCTION OF ANTIBODIES

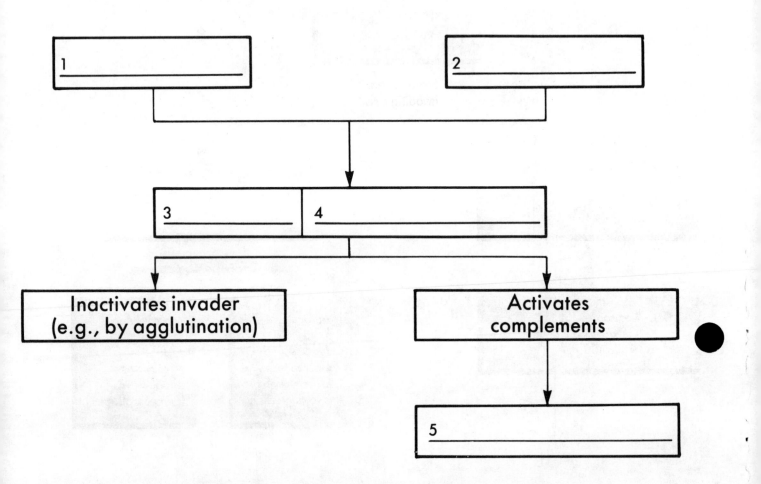

Inactivates invader
(e.g., by agglutination)

Activates
complements

148

CHAPTER 15

The Respiratory System

As you sit reviewing this system your body needs 16 quarts of air per minute. Walking requires 24 quarts of air, and running requires 50 quarts per minute. The respiratory system provides the air necessary for you to perform your daily activities and eliminates the waste gases from the air that you breath. Take a deep breath, and think of the air as entering some 250 million tiny air sacs similar in appearance to clusters of grapes. These microscopic air sacs expand to let air in and contract to force it out. These tiny sacs, or alveoli, are the functioning units of the respiratory system. They provide the necessary volume of oxygen and eliminate carbon dioxide 24 hours a day.

Air enters either through the mouth or the nasal cavity. It next passes through the pharynx and past the epiglottis, through the glottis and the rest of the larynx. It then continues down the trachea, into the bronchi to the bronchioles, and finally through the alveoli. The reverse occurs for expelled air.

The exchange of gases between air in the lungs and in the blood is known as external respiration. The exchange of gases that occurs between the blood and the cells of the body is known as internal respiration. By constantly supplying adequate oxygen and by removing carbon dioxide as it forms, the respiratory system helps to maintain an environment conducive to maximum cell efficiency.

Your review of this system is necessary to provide you with an understanding of this essential homeostatic mechanism.

TOPICS FOR REVIEW

Before progressing to Chapter 16, you should have an understanding of the structure and function of the organs of the respiratory system. Your review should include knowledge of the mechanisms responsible for both internal and external respiration. Your study should conclude with a knowledge of the volumes of air exchanged in pulmonary ventilation, an understanding of how respiration is regulated, and the common disorders of the respiratory tract.

STRUCTURAL PLAN
RESPIRATORY TRACTS
RESPIRATORY MUCOSA

Match the term with the definition.

a. Diffusion
b. Respiratory membrane
c. Alveoli
d. Capillaries
e. Respiration

f. Respiratory mucosa
g. Upper respiratory tract
h. Lower respiratory tract
i. Cilia
j. Air distributor

_____ 1. Function of respiratory system
_____ 2. Pharynx
_____ 3. Passive transport process responsible for actual exchange of gases

_____ 4. Assists with the movement of mucus toward the pharynx
_____ 5. Barrier between the blood in the capillaries and the air in the alveolus
_____ 6. Lines the tubes of the respiratory tree
_____ 7. Terminal air sacs
_____ 8. Trachea
_____ 9. Surround alveoli
_____ 10. Homeostatic mechanism

Fill in the blanks.

The organs of the respiratory system are designed to perform two basic functions. They serve as an:

(11) _____ _____ and as a (12) _____ _____. In addition to the above, the

respiratory system (13) _____, (14) _____, and (15) _____ the air we breath.

Respiratory organs include the (16) _____, (17) _____, (18) _____, (19)

_____, (20) _____, and the (21) _____. The respiratory system ends in millions of tiny,

thin-walled sacs called (22) _____. (23) _____ of gases takes place in these sacs. Two aspects

of the structure of these sacs assist them in the exchange of gases. First, an extremely thin membrane, the (24)

_____ _____ allows for easy exchange, and second, the large number of air sacs makes an

enormous (25) _____ area.

▸ If you have had difficulty with this section, review pages 376-379. ◂

NOSE
PHARYNX
LARYNX
DISORDERS OF UPPER RESPIRATORY TRACT

Circle the word or phrase that does <u>not</u> belong.

26. Nares	Septum	Oropharynx	Conchae
27. Conchae	Frontal	Maxillary	Sphenoidal
28. Oropharynx	Throat	5 inches	Epiglottis
29. Pharyngeal	Adenoids	Uvula	Nasopharynx
30. Middle ear	Tubes	Nasopharynx	Larynx
31. Voice box	Thyroid cartilage	Tonsils	Vocal cords
32. Palatine	Eustachian tube	Tonsils	Oropharynx
33. Pharynx	Epiglottis	Adam's apple	Voice box

150

Choose the correct response.

(a) Nose   (b) Pharynx   (c) Larynx

_____34. Warms and humidifies air
_____35. Air and food passes through here
_____36. Sinuses
_____37. Conchae
_____38. Septum
_____39. Tonsils
_____40. Middle ear infections
_____41. Epiglottis
_____42. Rhinitis
_____43. Sore throat
_____44. Epistaxis

▶ If you have had difficulty with this section, review pages 379-383. ◀

TRACHEA
BRONCHI, BRONCHIOLES AND ALVEOLI
LUNGS AND PLEURA

Fill in the blanks.

45. The windpipe is more properly referred to as the _____.

46. _____ keeps the framework of the trachea almost noncollapsible.

47. A lifesaving technique designed to free the trachea of ingested food or foreign objects is the _____.

48. The first branch or division of the trachea leading to the lungs is the _____.

49. Each alveolar duct ends in several _____.

50. The narrow part of each lung, up under the collarbone, is its _____.

51. The _____ covers the outer surface of the lungs and lines the inner surface of the rib cage.

52. Inflammation of the lining of the thoracic cavity is _____.

53. The presence of air in the pleural space on one side of the chest is a _____.

▶ If you have had difficulty with this section, review pages 383-388. ◀

RESPIRATION

*Mark **T** if the answer is true. If the answer is false, circle the incorrect word(s) and correct the statement.*

_____54. Diffusion is the process that moves air into and out of the lungs.
_____55. For inspiration to take place, the diaphragm and other respiratory muscles relax.
_____56. Diffusion is a passive process that results in movement up a concentration gradient.

_____57. The exchange of gases that occurs between blood in tissue capillaries and the body cells is external respiration.

_____58. Many pulmonary volumes can be measured as a person breathes into a spirometer.

_____59. Ordinarily we take about 2 pints of air into our lungs.

_____60. The amount of air normally breathed in and out with each breath is called tidal volume.

_____61. The largest amount of air that one can breathe out in one expiration is called residual volume.

_____62. The inspiratory reserve volume is the amount of air that can be forcibly inhaled after a normal inspiration.

► If you have had difficulty with this section, review pages 389-393. ◄

Circle the best answer.

63. The term that means the same thing as breathing is:

a. Gas exchange
b. Respiration
c. Inspiration

d. Expiration
e. Pulmonary ventilation

64. Carbaminohemoglobin is formed when _____ binds to hemoglobin.

a. Oxygen
b. Amino acids
c. Carbon dioxide

d. Nitrogen
e. None of the above is correct

65. Most of the oxygen transported by the blood is:

a. Dissolved to white blood cells
b. Bound to white blood cells
c. Bound to hemoglobin
d. Bound to carbaminohemoglobin
e. None of the above is correct

66. Which of the following would _not_ cause inspiration?

a. Elevation of the ribs
b. Elevation of the diaphragm
c. Contraction of the diaphragm
d. Chest cavity becomes longer from top to bottom

67. A young adult male would have a vital capacity of about _____ ml.

a. 500
b. 1,200
c. 3,300

d. 4,800
e. 6,200

68. The amount of air that can be forcibly exhaled after expiring the tidal volume is known as the:

a. Total lung capacity
b. Vital capacity
c. Inspiratory reserve volume

d. Expiratory reserve volume
e. None of the above is correct

69. Which one of the following is correct?

    a. VC = TV - IRV + ERV
    b. VC = TV + IRV - ERV
    c. VC = TV + IRV x ERV
    d. VC = TV + IRV + ERV
    e. None of the above is correct

▶ If you have had difficulty with this section, review pages 389-393. ◀

REGULATION OF RESPIRATION
RECEPTORS INFLUENCING RESPIRATION
TYPES OF BREATHING

Match the term on the left with the proper selection on the right.

_____ 70. Inspiratory center
_____ 71. Chemoreceptors
_____ 72. Pulmonary stretch receptors
_____ 73. Dyspnea
_____ 74. Respiratory arrest
_____ 75. Eupnea
_____ 76. Hypoventilation

a. Difficult breathing
b. Located in carotid bodies
c. Slow and shallow respirations
d. Normal respiratory rate
e. Located in the medulla
f. Failure to resume breathing following a period of apnea
g. Located throughout pulmonary airways and in the alveoli

▶ If you have had difficulty with this section, review pages 394-396. ◀

DISORDERS OF THE LOWER RESPIRATORY TRACT

Fill in the blanks.

77. _____ is an acute inflammation of the lungs in which the alveoli and bronchi become plugged with thick fluid.

78. Still a major cause of death in many poor, densely populated regions of the world, it has recently reemerged as an important health problem in some major U.S. cities. It is _____.

79. _____ may result from the progression of chronic bronchitis or other conditions as air becomes trapped within alveoli and causes them to enlarge and eventually rupture.

80. _____ is an obstructive disorder characterized by recurring spasms of the smooth muscle in the walls of the bronchial air passages.

▶ If you have had difficulty with this section, review pages 398-399. ◀

SAGITTAL VIEW OF FACE AND NECK

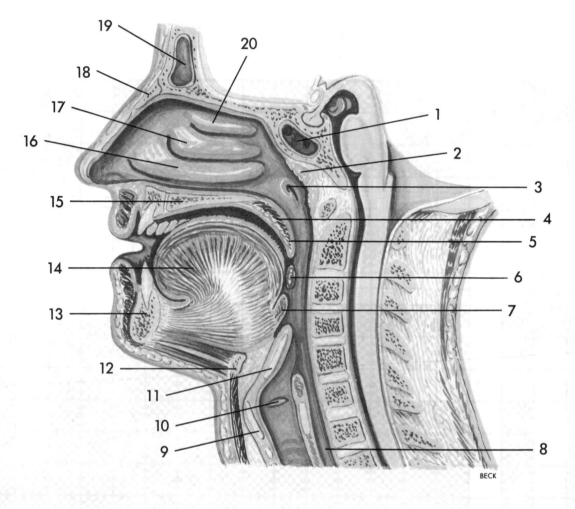

BECK

1. _____
2. _____
3. _____
4. _____
5. _____
6. _____
7. _____
8. _____
9. _____
10. _____

11. _____
12. _____
13. _____
14. _____
15. _____
16. _____
17. _____
18. _____
19. _____
20. _____

RESPIRATORY ORGANS

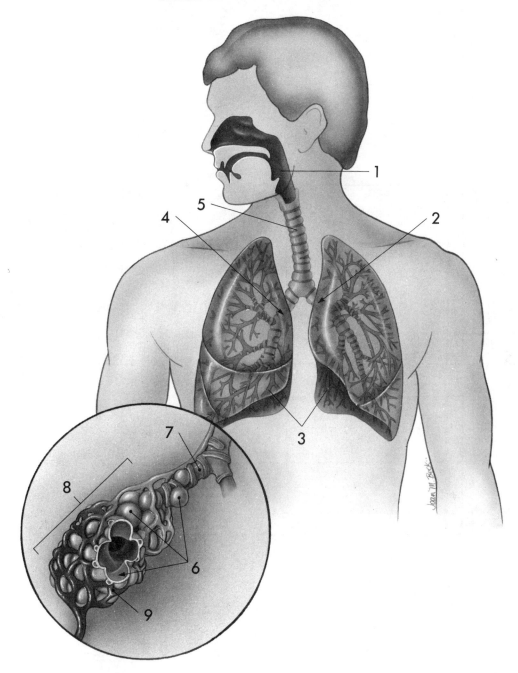

1. _____   6. _____

2. _____   7. _____

3. _____   8. _____

4. _____   9. _____

5. _____

PULMONARY VENTILATION VOLUMES

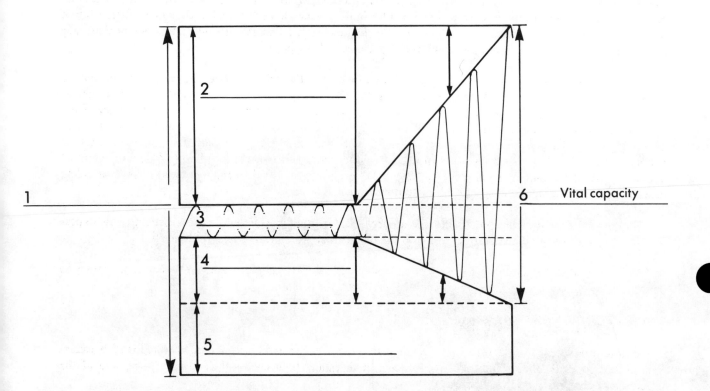

1
2
3
4
5
6   Vital capacity

1. _____   4. _____

2. _____   5. _____

3. _____

CHAPTER 16

The Digestive System

Think of the last meal you ate. The different shapes, sizes, tastes and textures that you so recently enjoyed. Think of those items circulating in your bloodstream in those same original shapes and sizes. Impossible? Of course. And because of this impossibility you will begin to understand and marvel at the close relationship of the digestive system to the circulatory system. It is the digestive system that changes our food, both mechanically and chemically, into a form that is acceptable to the blood and the body.

This change begins the moment you take the very first bite. Digestion starts in the mouth, where food is chewed and mixed with saliva. It then moves down the pharynx and esophagus by peristalsis and enters the stomach. In the stomach it is churned and mixed with gastric juices to become chyme. The chyme goes from the stomach into the duodenum where it is further broken down chemically by intestinal fluids, bile, and pancreatic juice. Those secretions prepare the food for absorption all along the course of the small intestine. Products that are not absorbed pass on through the entire length of the small intestine (duodenum, jejunum, ileum). From there they enter into the cecum of the large intestine, the ascending colon, transverse colon, descending colon, sigmoid colon, into the rectum and out the anus.

Products that are used in the cells undergo absorption. Absorption allows newly processed nutrients to pass through the walls of the digestive tract and into the bloodstream to be distributed to the cells.

Your review of this system will help you understand the mechanical and chemical processes necessary to convert food into energy sources and compounds necessary for survival.

TOPICS FOR REVIEW

Before progressing to Chapter 17, you should review the structure and function of all the organs of digestion. You should have an understanding of the process of digestion, both chemical and mechanical, and of the processes of absorption and metabolism.

WALL OF THE DIGESTIVE SYSTEM

Fill in the blanks.

1. The organs of the digestive system form an irregular-shaped tube called the alimentary canal or _____ _____.

2. The churning of food in the stomach is an example of the _____ breakdown of food.

3. _____ breakdown occurs when digestive enzymes act on food as it passes through the digestive tract.

4. Waste material resulting from the digestive process is known as _____.

5. Foods undergo three kinds of processing in the body: _____, _____, and _____.

6. The serosa of the digestive tube is composed of the _____ _____ in the abdominal cavity.

7. The digestive tract extends from the _____ to the _____.

8. The inside or hollow space within the alimentary canal is called the _____.

9. The inside layer of the digestive tract is the _____.

10. The connective tissue layer that lies beneath the lining of the digestive tract is the _____.

11. The muscularis contracts and moves food through the gastrointestinal tract by a process known as _____.

12. The outermost covering of the digestive tube is the _____.

13. The loops of the digestive tract are anchored to the posterior wall of the abdominal cavity by the _____.

Select the correct response from the two choices given and insert the letter in the answer blank.

(a) Main organ

(b) Accessory organ

_____14. Mouth
_____15. Parotids
_____16. Liver
_____17. Stomach
_____18. Cecum
_____19. Esophagus
_____20. Rectum
_____21. Pharynx
_____22. Appendix
_____23. Teeth
_____24. Gallbladder
_____25. Pancreas

▸ If you have had difficulty with this section, review pages 404-405. ◂

MOUTH
TEETH
SALIVARY GLANDS

Circle the best answer.

26. Which one of the following is *not* a part of the roof of the mouth?

a. Uvula
b. Palatine bones
c. Maxillary bones

d. Soft palate
e. All of the above are part of the roof of the mouth

27. The largest of the papillae on the surface of the tongue are the:

a. Filiform
b. Fungiform
c. Vallate
d. Taste buds

28. The first baby tooth, on an average, appears at:

a. 2 months
b. 1 year
c. 3 months
d. 1 month
e. 6 months

29. The portion of the tooth that is covered with enamel is the:

a. Pulp cavity
b. Neck
c. Root
d. Crown
e. None of the above is correct

30. The wall of the pulp cavity is surrounded by:

a. Enamel
b. Dentin
c. Cementum
d. Connective tissue
e. Blood and lymphatic vessels

31. Which of the following teeth is missing from the deciduous arch?

a. Central incisor
b. Canine
c. Second premolar
d. First molar
e. Second molar

32. The permanent central incisor erupts between the ages of _____.

a. 9-13
b. 5-6
c. 7-10
d. 7-8
e. None of the above is correct

33. The third molar appears between the ages of _____.

a. 10-14
b. 5-8
c. 11-16
d. 17-24
e. None of the above is correct

34. A general term for infection of the gums is known as:

a. Dental caries
b. Leukoplakia
c. Vincent's angina
d. Gingivitis

35. The ducts of the _____ glands open into the floor of the mouth.

a. Sublingual
b. Submandibular
c. Parotid
d. Carotid

36. The volume of saliva secreted per day is about:

a. One half pint
b. One pint

c. One liter
d. One gallon

37. Mumps are an infection of the:

a. Parotid gland
b. Sublingual gland

c. Submandibular gland
d. Tonsils

38. Incisors are used during mastication to:

a. Cut
b. Piece

c. Tear
d. Grind

39. Another name for the third molar is:

a. Central incisor
b. Wisdom tooth

c. Canine
d. Lateral incisor

40. After food has been chewed, it is formed into a small rounded mass called a:

a. Moat
b. Chyme

c. Bolus
d. Protease

▶ If you have had difficulty with this section, review pages 406-411. ◀

PHARYNX
ESOPHAGUS
STOMACH

Fill in the blanks.

The (41) _____ is a tubelike structure that functions as part of both respiratory and digestive systems. It connects the mouth with the (42) _____. The esophagus serves as a passageway for movement of food from the pharynx to the (43) _____. Food enters the stomach by passing through the muscular (44) _____ _____ at the end of the esophagus. Contraction of the stomach mixes the food thoroughly with the gastric juices and breaks it down into a semisolid mixture called (45) _____.

The three divisions of the stomach are the (46) _____, (47) _____, and (48) _____.

Food is held in the stomach by the (49) _____ _____ muscle long enough for partial

digestion to occur. After food has been in the stomach for approximately 3 hours, the chyme will enter the (50)

_____.

Match the term with the correct definition.

a. Esophagus
b. Chyme
c. Peristalsis
d. Rugae
e. Ulcer

f. Greater curvature
g. Emesis
h. Tagamet
i. hiatal hernia
j. Lesser curvature

_____ 51. Stomach folds
_____ 52. Upper right border of stomach
_____ 53. Total emptying of stomach contents back through the cardiac sphincter, up the esophagus, and out of the mouth
_____ 54. 10-inch passageway
_____ 55. Drug used to treat ulcers
_____ 56. Semisolid mixture of stomach contents
_____ 57. Muscle contractions of the digestive system
_____ 58. Open wound in digestive system that is acted on by acidic gastric juice
_____ 59. Stomach pushes through the gap in the diaphragm.
_____ 60. Lower left border of stomach

▸ If you have had difficulty with this section, review pages 411-414. ◂

SMALL INTESTINE
LIVER AND GALLBLADDER
PANCREAS

Circle the best answer.

61. Which one is *not* part of the small intestine?

    a. Jejunum
    b. Ileum

    c. Cecum
    d. Duodenum

62. Which one of the following structures does *not* increase the surface area of the intestine for absorption?

    a. Plicae
    b. Rugae

    c. Villi
    d. Brush border

63. The union of the cystic duct and hepatic duct form the:

    a. Common bile duct
    b. Major duodenal papilla

    c. Minor duodenal papilla
    d. Pancreatic duct

64. Obstruction of the _____ will lead to jaundice.

    a. Hepatic duct
    b. Pancreatic duct

    c. Cystic duct
    d. None of the above

65. Each villus in the intestine contains a lymphatic vessel or _____ that serves to absorb lipid or fat materials from the chyme:

    a. Plica
    b. Lacteal

    c. Villa
    d. Microvilli

66. The middle third of the duodenum contains the:

    a. Islets
    b. Fundus
    c. Body

    d. Rugae
    e. Major duodenal papilla

67. Cholelithiasis is the term used to describe:

    a. Biliary colic
    b. Jaundice

    c. Portal hypertension
    d. Gall stones

68. The liver is an:

    a. Enzyme
    b. Endocrine organ

    c. Endocrine gland
    d. Exocrine gland

69. Fats in chyme stimulate the secretion of the hormone:

    a. Lipase
    b. Cholecystokinin

    c. Protease
    d. Amylase

70. The largest gland in the body is the:

    a. Pituitary
    b. Thyroid

    c. Liver
    d. Thymus

▸ If you have had difficulty with this section, review pages 415-418. ◂

LARGE INTESTINE
APPENDIX
PERITONEUM

*If the statement is true, mark **T** next to the answer. If the statement is false, circle the incorrect word(s) and write the correct term in the blank next to the statement.*

_____71. Bacteria in the large intestine are responsible for the synthesis of vitamin E needed for normal blood clotting.

_____72. Villi in the large intestine absorb salts and water.

_____73. If waste products pass rapidly through the large intestine, constipation results.

_____74. The ileocecal valve opens into the sigmoid colon.

_____75. The splenic flexure is the bend between the ascending colon and the transverse colon.

_____ 76. The splenic colon is the S-shaped segment that terminates in the rectum.
_____ 77. The appendix serves no important digestive function in humans.
_____ 78. For patients with suspected appendicitis, a physician will often evaluate the appendix by a digital rectal examination.
_____ 79. The visceral layer of the peritoneum lines the abdominal cavity.
_____ 80. The greater omentum is shaped like a fan and serves to anchor the small intestine to the posterior abdominal wall.
_____ 81. Diarrhea is an inflammation of abnormal saclike outpouchings of the intestinal wall.
_____ 82. Crohn's disease is a type of autoimmune colitis.
_____ 83. A colostomy is a surgical procedure in which an artificial anus is created on the abdominal wall.
_____ 84. Peritonitis is the abnormal accumulation of fluid in the peritoneal space.

► If you have had difficulty with this section, review pages 420-425. ◄

DIGESTION
ABSORPTION
METABOLISM

Circle the best answer.

85. Which one of the following substances does _not_ contain any enzymes?

   a. Saliva
   b. Bile
   c. Gastric juice

   d. Pancreatic juice
   e. Intestinal juice

86. Which one of the following is a simple sugar?

   a. Maltose
   b. Sucrose
   c. Lactose

   d. Glucose
   e. Starch

87. Cane sugar is the same as:

   a. Maltose
   b. Lactose
   c. Sucrose

   d. Glucose
   e. None of the above is correct

88. Most of the digestion of carbohydrates takes place in the:

   a. Mouth
   b. Stomach

   c. Small intestine
   d. Large intestine

89. Fats are broken down into:

   a. Amino acids
   b. Simple sugars

   c. Fatty acids
   d. Disaccharides

► If you have had difficulty with this section, review pages 426-427. ◄

90. *Fill in the blank areas on the chart below.*

CHEMICAL DIGESTION

DIGESTIVE JUICES AND ENZYMES	SUBSTANCE DIGESTED (OR HYDROLYZED)	RESULTING PRODUCT
SALIVA		
1. Amylase	1.	1. Maltose
GASTRIC JUICE		
2. Protease (pepsin) plus hydrochloric acid	2. Proteins	2.
PANCREATIC JUICE		
3. Protease (trypsin)	3. Amylase Proteins (intact or partially digested)	3.
4. Lipase	4.	4. Fatty acids and glycerol
INTESTINAL JUICE		
5. Peptidases	5.	5. Amino acids
6.	6. Sucrose	6. Glucose and fructose
7. Lactase	7.	7. Glucose and galactose (simple sugars)
8. Maltase	8. Maltose	8.

▸ If you have had difficulty with this section, review pages 426-427. ◂

APPLYING WHAT YOU KNOW

91. Mr. Gabriel was a successful businessman, but he worked too hard and was always under great stress. His doctor cautioned him that if he did not alter his style of living he would be subject to hyperacidity. What could be the resulting condition of hyperacidity?

92. Baby Shearer has been regurgitating his bottle feeding at every meal. The milk is curdled, but does not appear to be digested. He has become dehydrated, and so his mother is taking him to the pediatrician. What is a possible diagnosis from your textbook reading?

93. Mr. Josten has gained a great deal of weight suddenly. He also noticed that he was sluggish and always tired. What test might his physician order for him and for what reason?

94. **WORD FIND**

Can you find the terms listed below in the box of letters? Words may be spelled top to bottom, bottom to top, right to left, left to right, or diagonally.

```
W J A D L B T D N M X H R G S P R U B E
F B Q I M Z K N X O E C H B E T S V P C
H M D L V Y N J R I I Z D W E Y C U B I
S S E P F K O S W U D T E M G P W L T D
B A T A E K I E L M B N A J F Y D A F N
D E E P C W T D G F I T E C L J B I T U
D R O I E H S E P Z Y Q R P I L V M N A
I C L L S E N Q W T P A A P T G J B J
A N C L C U G T W H C F L F E A S O H P
R A A A H V I I E R Q K U X Y H O A S E
R P V E N F D N Y B U N B N Q E J N M R
H Z I U K W V J D S D E W Q T M N E M I
E E T N R N O U R U I A S O C U M Y E S
A F Y Z I M O R S F R D W D C L J U S T
G O J C J D S R C X C H C M I S Z G E A
I W U N E N O I T P R O S B A I C W N L
R D U N B S T O M A C H N F L F X Y T S
J L U H L I A M Q F Q F G T A Y B Z E I
J M Y L E Q A Y F J Z P J W Q C O J R S
Y M E T A B O L I S M M F T M Y M Q Y S
```

LIST OF WORDS

HEARTBURN
ABSORPTION
PERISTALSIS
MASTICATION
CAVITY
EMULSIFY
FUNDUS
MESENTERY

FECES
METABOLISM
PAPILLAE
CROWN
STOMACH
JAUNDICE
DIARRHEA

DIGESTION
MUCOSA
UVULA
DENTIN
PANCREAS
DUODENUM
APPENDIX

DID YOU KNOW?

The liver performs over 500 functions and produces over 1000 enzymes to handle the chemical conversions necessary for survival.

DIGESTIVE SYSTEM

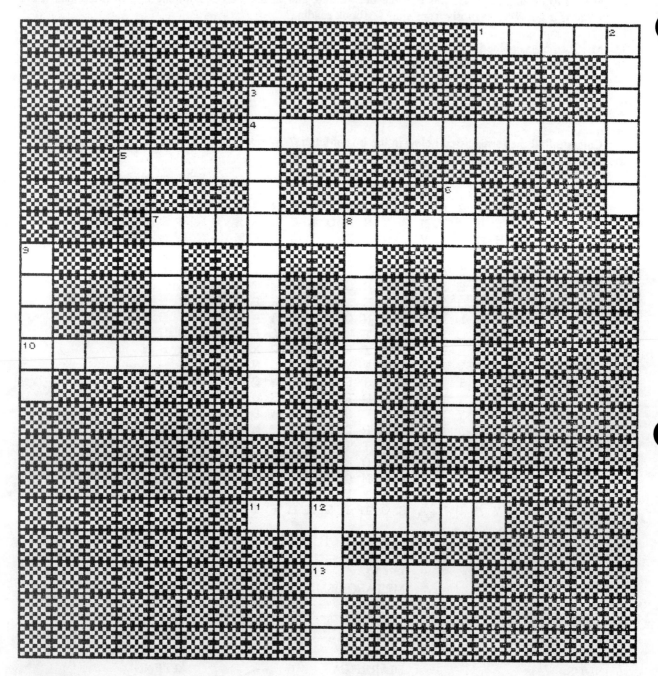

ACROSS

1. Stomach folds
4. Inflammation of the appendix
5. Waste product of digestion
7. Movement of food through digestive tract
10. Prevents food from entering nasal cavities
11. Yellowish skin discoloration
13. Semisolid mixture

DOWN

2. Vomitus
3. Process of chewing
6. Fluid stools
7. Intestinal folds
8. Digested food moves from intestine to blood
9. Rounded mass of food
12. Open wound in digestive area acted on by acid juices

LOCATION OF DIGESTIVE ORGANS

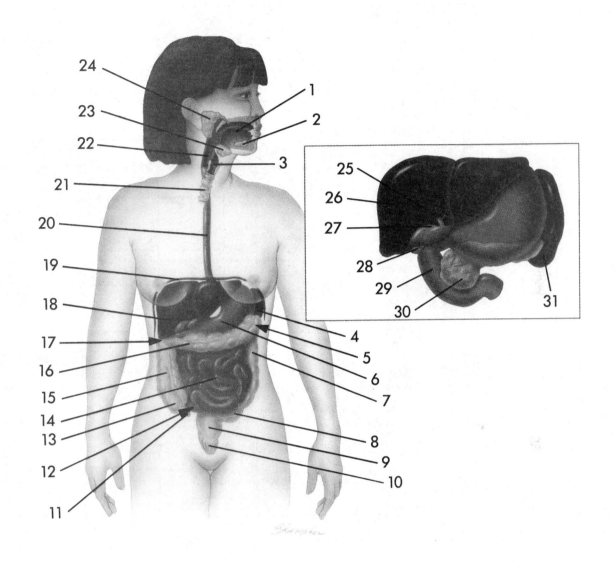

1. _____
2. _____
3. _____
4. _____
5. _____
6. _____
7. _____
8. _____
9. _____
10. _____
11. _____

12. _____
13. _____
14. _____
15. _____
16. _____
17. _____
18. _____
19. _____
20. _____
21. _____

22. _____
23. _____
24. _____
25. _____
26. _____
27. _____
28. _____
29. _____
30. _____
31. _____

TOOTH

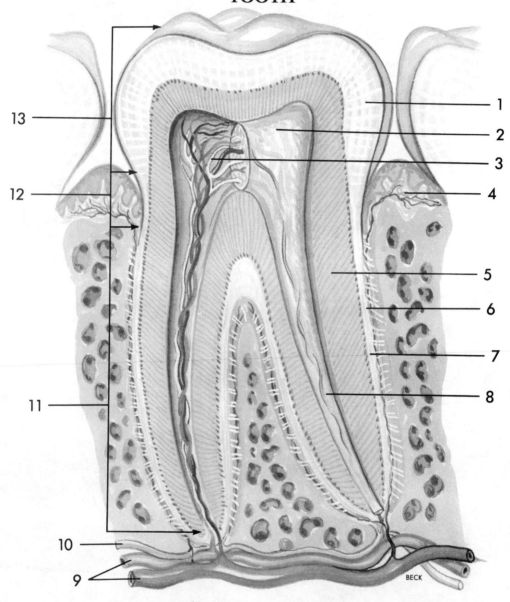

BECK

1. _____
2. _____
3. _____
4. _____
5. _____
6. _____
7. _____

8. _____
9. _____
10. _____
11. _____
12. _____
13. _____

THE SALIVARY GLANDS

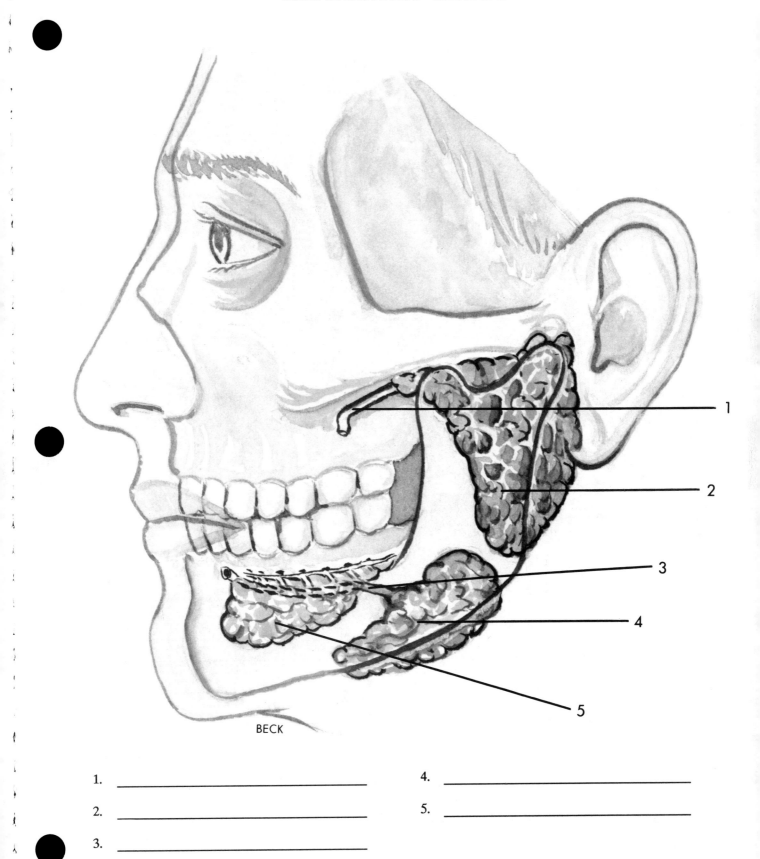

BECK

1. _____   4. _____

2. _____   5. _____

3. _____

STOMACH

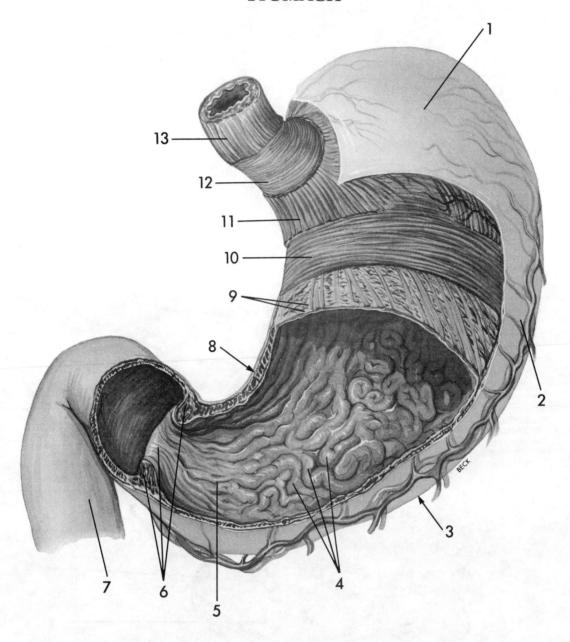

1. _____

2. _____

3. _____

4. _____

5. _____

6. _____

7. _____

8. _____

9. _____

10. _____

11. _____

12. _____

13. _____

GALLBLADDER AND BILE DUCTS

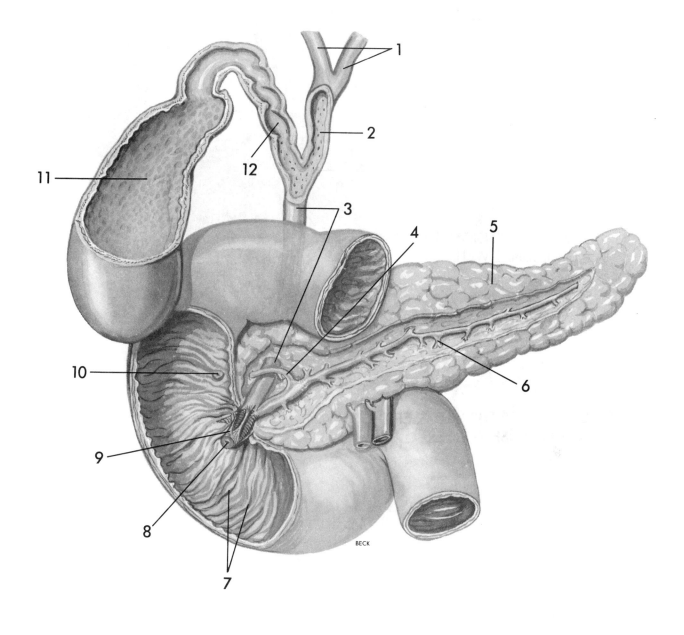

BECK

1. _____   7. _____

2. _____   8. _____

3. _____   9. _____

4. _____   10. _____

5. _____   11. _____

6. _____   12. _____

CHAPTER 17

Nutrition and Metabolism

Most of us love to eat, but do the foods we enjoy provide us with the basic food types necessary for good nutrition? The body, a finely tuned machine, requires a balance of carbohydrates, fats, proteins, vitamins, and minerals to function properly. These nutrients must be digested, absorbed, and circulated to cells constantly to accommodate the numerous activities that occur throughout the body. The use the body makes of foods once these processes are completed is called "metabolism."

The liver plays a major role in the metabolism of food. It helps maintain a normal blood glucose level, removes toxins from the blood, processes blood immediately after it leaves the gastrointestinal tract, and initiates the first steps of protein and fat metabolism.

This chapter also discusses basal metabolic rate (BMR). The BMR is the rate at which food is catabolized under basal conditions. This test and the protein-bound iodine (PBI) are indirect measures of thyroid gland functioning. The total metabolic rate (TMR) is the amount of energy, expressed in calories, used by the body each day.

Finally, maintaining a constant body temperature is a function of the hypothalamus and a challenge for the metabolic factors of the body. Review of this chapter is necessary to provide you with an understanding of the "fuel" or nutrition necessary to maintain your complex homeostatic machine—the body.

TOPICS FOR REVIEW

Before progressing to Chapter 18, you should be able to define and contrast catabolism and anabolism. Your review should include the metabolic roles of carbohydrates, fats, proteins, vitamins, and minerals. Your study should conclude with an understanding of the basal metabolic rate, physiological mechanisms that regulate body temperature, and the common metabolic and eating disorders.

THE ROLE OF THE LIVER

Fill in the blanks.

The liver plays an important role in the mechanical digestion of lipids because it secretes (1)

_____. It also produces two of the plasma proteins that play an essential role in blood clotting.

These two proteins are (2) _____ and (3) _____. Additionally liver cells store several

substances, notably vitamins A, D, K, and (4) _____.

Finally, the liver is assisted by a unique structural feature of the blood vessels that supply it. This

arrangement, known as the (5) _____, allows toxins to be removed from the bloodstream before

nutrients are distributed throughout the body.

NUTRIENT METABOLISM

Match the term with the definition.

(a) Carbohydrate   (b) Fat   (c) Protein
(d) Vitamins   (e) Minerals

_____ 6. Used if cells have inadequate amounts of glucose to catabolize
_____ 7. Preferred energy food
_____ 8. Amino acids
_____ 9. Fat soluble
_____ 10. Required for nerve conduction
_____ 11. Glycolysis
_____ 12. Inorganic elements found naturally in the earth
_____ 13. Pyruvic acid

Circle the word or phrase that does not belong.

14. Glycolysis	Citric acid cycle	ATP	Bile
15. Adipose	Amino acids	Energy	Glycerol
16. A	D	M	K
17. Pyruvic acid	Proteins	Amino acids	Energy
18. Hydrocortisone	Insulin	Growth hormone	Epinephrine
19. Sodium	Calcium	Zinc	Folic acid
20. Thiamine	Niacin	Ascorbic acid	Riboflavin

► If you have had difficulty with this section, review pages 434-439. ◄

METABOLIC AND EATING DISORDERS

Choose the correct response.

a. BMR   e. Obesity
b. Diabetes mellitus   f. PCM
c. Anorexia nervosa   g. Dysphagia
d. Bulimia   h. Glycosuria

_____ 21. Insulin deficiency is a symptom of this disorder
_____ 22. Behavioral disorder characterized by chronic refusal to eat
_____ 23. Difficulty in swallowing
_____ 24. Results from a deficiency of calories in general and protein in particular
_____ 25. Hypothyroidism will affect this measurement
_____ 26. Loss of glucose in urine
_____ 27. Symptom of chronic overeating behavior

_____28. Behavioral disorder characterized by insatiable craving for food alternating with periods of self-deprivation.

▸ If you have had difficulty with this section, review pages 442-443. ◂

METABOLIC RATES
BODY TEMPERATURE

Circle the correct choice.

29. The rate at which food is catabolized under basal conditions is the:

    a. TMR c. BMR
    b. PBI d. ATP

30. The total amount of energy used by the body per day is the:

    a. TMR c. BMR
    b. PBI d. ATP

31. Over _____ of the energy released from food molecules during catabolism is converted to heat rather than being transferred to ATP.

    a. 20% c. 60%
    b. 40% d. 80%

32. Maintaining thermoregulation is a function of the:

    a. Thalamus c. Thyroid
    b. Hypothalamus d. Parathyroids

33. A transfer of heat energy to the skin, then the external environment is:

    a. Radiation c. Convection
    b. Conduction d. Evaporation

34. A flow of heat waves away from the blood is known as:

    a. Radiation c. Convection
    b. Conduction d. Evaporation

35. A transfer of heat energy to air that is continually flowing away from the skin is known as:

    a. Radiation c. Convection
    b. Conduction d. Evaporation

36. Heat that is absorbed by the process of water vaporization is called:

    a. Radiation c. Convection
    b. Conduction d. Evaporation

37. A/an _____ is the amount of energy needed to raise the temperature of one gram of water one degree Celsius.

   a. Calorie
   b. Kilocalorie

   c. ATP
   d. BMR

▶ If you have had difficulty with this section, review pages 440-445. ◀

ABNORMAL BODY TEMPERATURE

*Mark **T** if the answer is true. If the answer is false, circle the wrong word(s) and correct the statement by inserting the proper word(s) in the answer blank.*

_____38. Pyrogens cause the thermostatic control centers of the hypothalamus to produce a fever.

_____39. Malignant hyperthermia is the inability to maintain a normal body temperature in extremely cold environments.

_____40. Frostbite is local damage to tissues caused by extremely low temperatures.

_____41. Heat exhaustion is characterized by body temperatures of 41 degrees Celsius or higher.

_____42. Dantrium is used to prevent or relieve the effects of frostbite.

▶ If you have had difficulty with this section, review pages 445-446. ◀

180

Unscramble the words.

43. LRIEV

44. TAOBALICMS

45. OMNIA

46. YPURCVI

Take the circled letters, unscramble them, and fill in the statement.

How the magician paid his bills.

47.

abracadabra!

APPLYING WHAT YOU KNOW

48. Dr. Ellis was concerned about Deborrah. Her daily food intake provided fewer calories than her TMR. If this trend continues, what will be the result? If it continues over a long period of time, what eating disorder might Deborrah develop?

49. Lisa Kennedy was experiencing fatigue and a blood test revealed that she was slightly anemic. What mineral will her doctor most likely prescribe? What dietary sources might you suggest that she emphasize in her daily intake?

181

50. WORD FIND

Can you find the terms listed below in the box of letters? Words may be spelled top to bottom, bottom to top, right to left, left to right, or diagonally.

```
M I N E R A L S N K Y O H N K N I A L P
W B G K C F B M Z M C O N V E C T I O N
P J Z C V A H C I B P P J J R M T Z A I
B P U S X J R S I X O J O A E S L J C I
R T C D G R X B Y R A D I A T I O N A E
S A B I B O B U O H S A A V V F Y V T X
M Y A K Y Q L C W H C A E Y U F V L A K
Q E U P N L K U N G Y P Y N M S Q K B V
N T F Q Y F G R V R N D L H O R U G O X
O U E A F T X M T B L O R E C Y L G L H
I T H P T V B Q B M R Q C A F G V I I D
T X A Q G S U I Y R E V I L T D Y J S F
C L J O Y H F V T W I E Q G K E Z J M U
U Z C B C P O W F I A I N W E B S F Z D
D S N I E T O R P V Z R V G B Q P N C H
N J Y K J Z E Z Y A D I P O S E P Y J P
O K V X L V Q N N O I T A R O P A V E N
C Y O Z S Z Q M O F E L I B Z S U J Y G
A F Q H M S I S Y L O C Y L G P F H E K
O D I A A Q R Q V I T A M I N S U A U Q
```

LIST OF WORDS

LIVER	CARBOHYDRATES	FATS
PROTEINS	VITAMINS	MINERALS
GLYCOLYSIS	ATP	BILE
ADIPOSE	GLYCEROL	CATABOLISM
PBI	BMR	TMR
RADIATION	CONDUCTION	CONVECTION
EVAPORATION		

DID YOU KNOW?

The amount of energy required to raise a 200-pound man 15 feet is about the amount of energy in one large calorie.

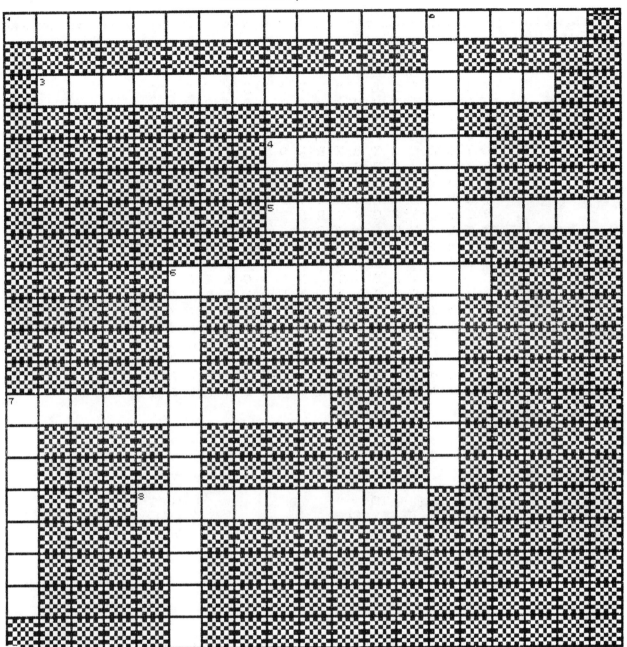

ACROSS

1. Rate of metabolism when a person is lying down, but awake (three words)
3. Maintaining homeostasis of body temperature
4. Organic molecule needed in small quantities for normal metabolism throughout the body
5. A unit of measure for heat, also known as a large calorie
6. Takes place in the cytoplasm of a cell and changes glucose to pyruvic acid
7. Breaks food molecules down releasing stored energy
8. Builds food molecules into complex substances

DOWN

2. An aerobic process which changes pyruvic acid to carbon dioxide
6. A series of reactions that join glucose molecules together to form glycogen
7. Amount of energy needed to raise the temperature of one gram of water one degree Celsius

CHAPTER 18

The Urinary System

Living produces wastes. Wherever people live or work or play, wastes accumulate. To keep these areas healthy, there must be a method of disposing of these wastes such as a sanitation department.

Wastes accumulate in your body also. The conversion of food and gases into substances and energy necessary for survival results in waste products. A large percentage of these wastes is removed by the urinary system.

Two vital organs, the kidneys, cleanse the blood of the many waste products that are continually produced as a result of the metabolism of food in the body cells. They eliminate these wastes in the form of urine.

Urine formation is the result of three processes: filtration, reabsorption, and secretion. These processes occur in successive portions of the microscopic units of the kidneys known as nephrons. The amount of urine produced by the nephrons is controlled primarily by two hormones, ADH and aldosterone.

After urine is produced it is drained from the renal pelvis by the ureters to flow into the bladder. The bladder then stores the urine until it is voided through the urethra.

If waste products are allowed to accumulate in the body, they soon become poisonous, a condition called uremia. A knowledge of the urinary system is necessary to understand how the body rids itself of waste and avoids toxicity.

TOPICS FOR REVIEW

Before progressing to Chapter 19 you should have an understanding of the structure and function of the organs of the urinary system. Your review should include knowledge of the nephron and its role in urine production. Your study should conclude with a review of the three main processes involved in urine production, the mechanisms that control urine volume, and the major renal and urinary disorders.

KIDNEYS

Circle the correct choice.

1. The outermost portion of the kidney is known as the:

   a. Medulla
   b. Papilla
   c. Pelvis

   d. Pyramid
   e. Cortex ✓

2. The saclike structure that surrounds the glomerulus is the:

   a. Renal pelvis
   b. Calyx
   c. Bowman's capsule ✓

   d. Cortex
   e. None of the above is correct

3. The renal corpuscle is made up of the:

    a. Bowman's capsule and proximal convoluted tubule
    b. Glomerulus and proximal convoluted tubule
    c. Bowman's capsule and the distal convoluted tubule
    d. Glomerulus and the distal convoluted tubule
    e. Bowman's capsule and the glomerulus

4. Which of the following functions is *not* performed by the kidneys?

    a. Help maintain homeostasis
    b. Remove wastes from the blood
    c. Produce ADH
    d. Remove electrolytes from the blood

5. _____99_____% of the glomerular filtrate is reabsorbed.

    a. 20
    b. 40
    c. 75

    d. 85
    e. 99

6. The glomerular filtration rate is _____125_____ ml per minute.

    a. 1.25
    b. 12.5
    c. 125.0

    d. 1250.0
    e. None of the above is correct

7. Glucose is mostly reabsorbed in the:

    a. Loop of Henle
    b. Proximal convoluted tubule
    c. Distal convoluted tubule
    d. Glomerulus
    e. None of the above is correct.

8. Reabsorption does *not* occur in the:

    a. Loop of Henle
    b. Proximal convoluted tubule
    c. Distal convoluted tubule

    d. Collecting tubules
    e. Calyx

9. The greater the amount of salt intake the:

    a. Less salt excreted in the urine
    b. More salt is reabsorbed
    c. The more salt excreted in the urine
    d. None of the above is correct.

10. Which one of the following substances is secreted by diffusion:

    a. Sodium ions
    b. Certain drugs
    c. Ammonia

    d. Hydrogen ions
    e. Potassium ions

11. Which of the following statements about ADH is *not* correct?

    a. It is stored by the pituitary gland
    b. It makes the collecting tubules less permeable to water
    c. It makes the distal convoluted tubules more permeable
    d. It is produced by the hypothalamus

12. Which of the following statements about aldosterone is *not* correct?

    a. It is secreted by the adrenal cortex
    b. It is a water-retaining hormone
    c. It is a salt-retaining hormone
    d. All of the above are correct

Choose the correct term and write its letter in the space next to the appropriate definition below.

a. Medulla
b. Cortex
c. Pyramids
d. Papilla
e. Pelvis
f. Calyx
g. Nephrons

h. Uremia
i. Catheterization
j. Bowman's capsule
k. Glomerulus
l. Loop of Henle

    G 13. Functioning unit of urinary system
    I 14. Passage of a hollow tube through the urethra into the bladder for withdrawing urine
    H 15. Uremic poisoning
    B 16. Outer part of kidney
    K 17. Together with Bowman's capsule forms renal corpuscle
    F 18. Division of the renal pelvis
    J 19. Cup-shaped top of a nephron
    D 20. Innermost end of a pyramid
    L 21. Extension of proximal tubule
    C 22. Triangular-shaped divisions of the medulla of the kidney
    E 23. An expansion of the upper end of a ureter
    A 24. Inner portion of kidney

▸ If you have had difficulty with this section, review pages 452-457. ◂

URETERS
URINARY BLADDER
URETHRA

Indicate which organ is identified by the following descriptions by inserting the appropriate letter in the answer blank.

(a) Ureters   (b) Bladder   (c) Urethra

    C 25. Between urinary meatus and bladder
    B 26. Rugae
    C 27. Lower-most part of urinary tract
    A 28. Lining membrane richly supplied with sensory nerve endings

_B_ 29. Lies behind pubic symphysis
_C_ 30. Dual function in male
_C_ 31. 1½ inches long in female
_A_ 32. Drains renal pelvis
_C_ 33. Surrounded by prostate in male
_B_ 34. Elastic fibers and involuntary muscle fibers
_A_ 35. 10 to 12 inches long
_B_ 36. Trigone

Fill in the blanks.

37. The physical, chemical, and microscopic examination of urine is termed _urinalysis_.

38. The urinary tract is lined with _mucous_ _membrane_.

39. Urine specimens are often spun in a _centrifuge_ to force suspended particles to the bottom of a test tube.

40. The absence of urine is known as _anuria_.

41. Clinical studies have proved that improper catheterization techniques cause _UTI_ in hospitalized patients.

42. In the male, the urethra serves a dual function: a passageway for urine and _semen_.

43. The external opening of the urethra is the _urinary external meatus_.

▸ If you have had difficulty with this section, review pages 452-463. ◂

MICTURITION

Fill in the blanks.

The terms (44) _micturition_, (45) _urination_ and (46) _voiding_ all refer to the passage of urine from the body or the emptying of the bladder. The sphincters guard the bladder. The (47) _internal urethral sphincter_ is the sphincter located at the bladder (48) _exit_ and is involuntary. The external urethral sphincter circles the (49) _urethra_ and is under (50) _voluntary_ control.

As the bladder fills, nervous impulses are transmitted to the spinal cord and an (51) _emptying reflex_ _urethra_ is initiated. Urine then enters the (52) _urethra_ to be eliminated.

Urinary (53) _retention_ is a condition in which no urine is voided. Urinary (54) _suppression_ is when the kidneys do not produce any urine, but the bladder retains its ability to empty itself. Complete

188

destruction or transection of the sacral cord produces an (55) _automatic bladder_.

► If you have had difficulty with this section, review page 463. ◄

RENAL AND URINARY DISORDERS

Select the correct disorder from the clues that are provided.

a. Pyelonephritis
b. Renal colic
c. Renal calculi
d. Acute glomerulonephritis
e. Proteinuria
f. Hematuria

g. Neurogenic bladder
h. Acute renal failure
i. Hydronephrosis
j. Chronic renal failure
k. Cystitis
l. Urethritis

_____56. Urine backs up into the kidneys causing swelling of renal pelvis and calyces.
_____57. Kidney stones
_____58. Involuntary retention of urine with subsequent distention of the bladder
_____59. Blood in the urine
_____60. Inflammation of the bladder
_____61. Inflammation of the renal pelvis and connective tissues of the kidney
_____62. An abrupt reduction in kidney function characterized by oliguria and a sharp rise in nitrogenous compounds in the blood.
_____63. Progressive condition resulting from gradual loss of nephrons
_____64. Intense kidney pain caused by obstruction of the ureters by large kidney stones
_____65. Most common form of kidney disease caused by a delayed immune response to streptococcal infection
_____66. Albumin in the urine
_____67. Inflammation of the urethra that commonly results from bacterial infection

► If you have had difficulty with this section, review pages 464-468. ◄

APPLYING WHAT YOU KNOW

68. John suffered from low levels of ADH. What primary urinary symptom would he notice?

69. Bud was in a diving accident and his spinal cord was severed. He was paralyzed from the waist down and as a result was incontinent. His physician was concerned about the continuous residual urine buildup. What was the reason for concern?

70. WORD FIND

Can you find the terms listed below in the box of letters? Words may be spelled top to bottom, bottom to top, right to left, left to right, or diagonally.

```
B X Z X Z M E T H J Z G I R S C F U V X
F W N E P H R O N S I T I T S Y C K Y P
U Z B X Y Q E I A L L U D E M L D R E O
R J T M D P E R Q M C O R T E X J L N K
E S O W E B X D S E P H L X A Y U R D M
T U U L Q N S A X R E V A F B O O E I Z
E Z V H R X Z N K M G J H A G W J D K U
R I J L D H E Z O F I L T R A T I O N B
S H F J L K L D X T C P O N D Y D R B T
B P X I U E I Q Z W D Y X M O M I E M J
T J S Y H A A D H B P R U I E A I D S V
W F Z H L J O I N A N A C P B R S D B C
L D Q Y X A Q L P C Q M Q A W E U A C F
H Q S W C U C I R C G I P A L Y L L J X
R I W F Y B L E K E R D V S L C D B U I
S C F C H L O R N I A S Y C U S U Q L S
M R S T A Y Z K L M S V J I U A H L Q H
B K Q K Z N M T X R I H T K P I S V I D
J G D B E C N E N I T N O C N I P V E M
V A Z M I C T U R I T I O N L V I J I H
```

LIST OF WORDS

MEDULLA
PAPILLA
GLOMERULUS
FILTRATION
ADH
KIDNEY

CORTEX
PELVIS
CALCULI
NEPHRON
URETERS
MICTURITION

PYRAMIDS
CALYX
INCONTINENCE
HEMODIALYSIS
BLADDER
CYSTITIS

DID YOU KNOW?

If the tubules in a kidney were stretched out and untangled, there would be 70 miles of them.

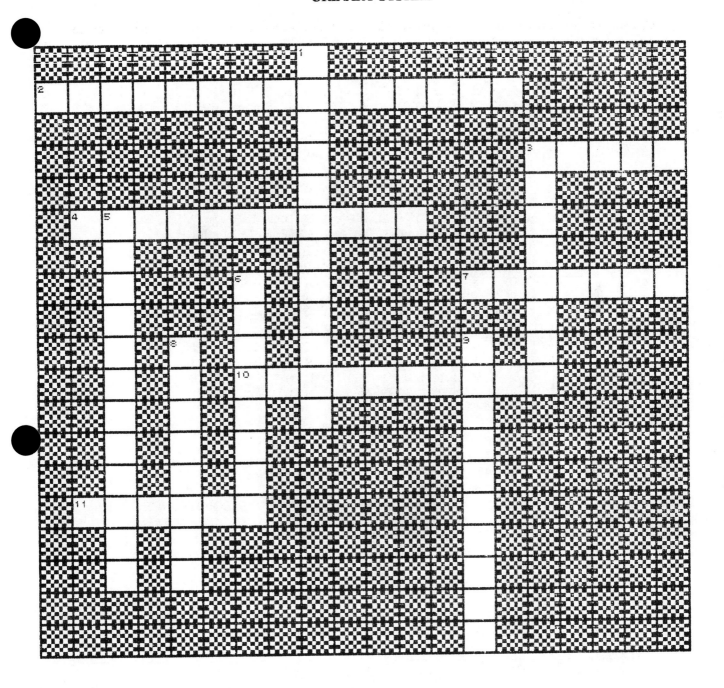

ACROSS

2. Passage of a tube into the bladder to withdraw urine
3. Division of the renal pelvis
4. Urination
7. Area on posterior bladder wall free of rugae
10. Network of blood capillaries tucked into Bowman's capsule
11. Absence of urine

DOWN

1. Ultrasound generator used to break up kidney stones
3. Bladder infection
5. Voiding involuntarily
6. Scanty urine
8. Large amount of urine
9. Glucose in the urine

URINARY SYSTEM

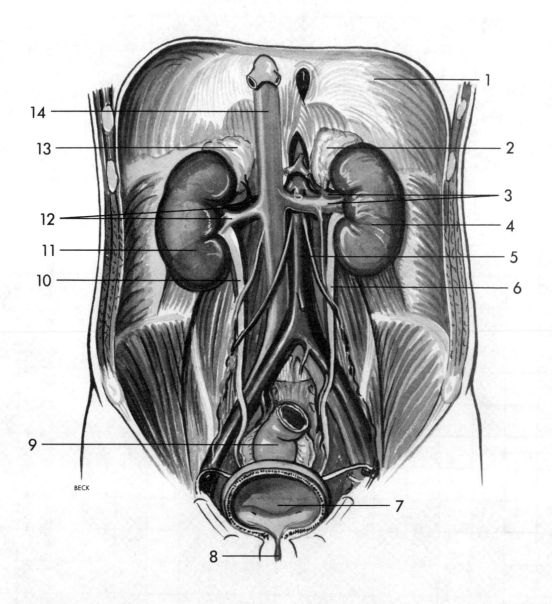

BECK

1. _____   8. _____

2. _____   9. _____

3. _____   10. _____

4. _____   11. _____

5. _____   12. _____

6. _____   13. _____

7. _____   14. _____

KIDNEY

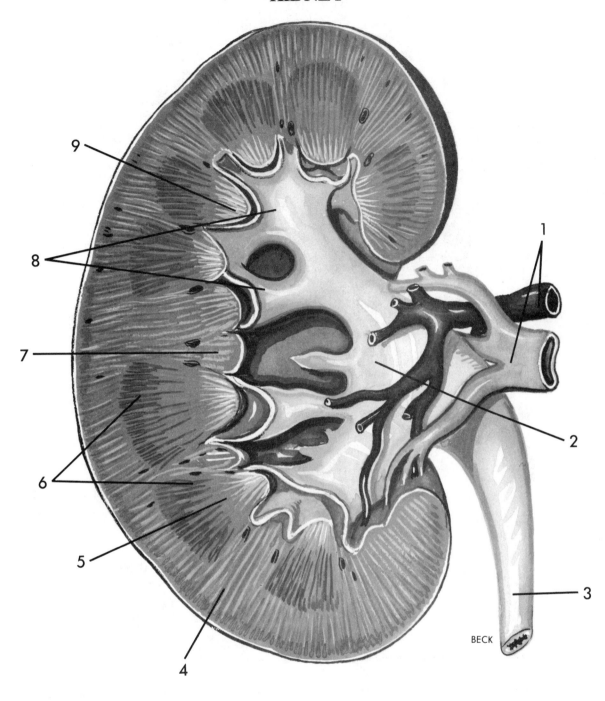

BECK

1. _____
2. _____
3. _____
4. _____
5. _____

6. _____
7. _____
8. _____
9. _____

NEPHRON

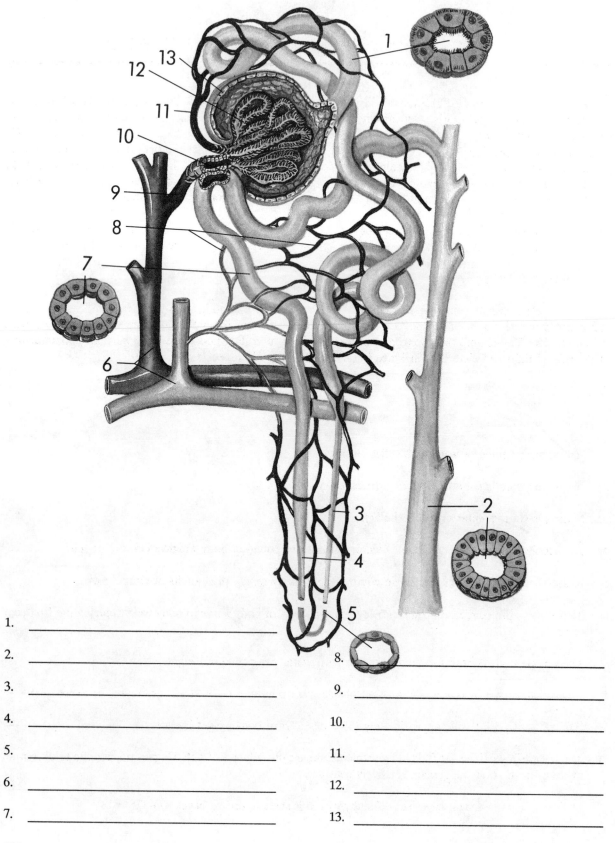

1. _____

2. _____

3. _____

4. _____

5. _____

6. _____

7. _____

8. _____

9. _____

10. _____

11. _____

12. _____

13. _____

CHAPTER 19

Fluid and Electrolyte Balance

Referring to the very first chapter in your text, you will recall that survival depends on the body's ability to maintain or restore homeostasis. Specifically, homeostasis means that the body fluids remain constant within very narrow limits. These fluids are classified as either intracellular fluid (ICF) or extracellular fluid (ECF). As their names imply, intracellular fluid lies within the cells and extracellular fluid is located outside the cells. A balance between these two fluids is maintained by certain body mechanisms. They are: (a) adjustment of fluid output to fluid intake under normal circumstances; (b) the concentration of electrolytes in the extracellular fluid; (c) the capillary blood pressure, and finally (d) the concentration of proteins in the blood.

Comprehension of how these mechanisms maintain and restore fluid balance is necessary for an understanding of the complexities of homeostasis and its relationship to the survival of the individual.

TOPICS FOR REVIEW

Before progressing to Chapter 20, you should review the types of body fluids and their subdivisions. Your study should include the mechanisms that maintain fluid balance and the nature and importance of electrolytes in body fluids. You should be able to give examples of common fluid imbalances, and have an understanding of the role of fluid and electrolyte balance in the maintenance of homeostasis.

BODY FLUIDS

Circle the correct answer.

1. The largest volume of water by far lies (inside or outside) cells.

2. Interstitial fluid is (intracellular or extracellular).

3. Plasma is (intracellular or extracellular).

4. Fat people have a (lower or higher) water content per pound of body weight than thin people.

5. Infants have (more or less) water in comparison to body weight than adults of either sex.

6. There is a rapid (increase or decline) in the proportion of body water to body weight during the first year of life.

7. The female body contains slightly (more or less) water per pound of weight.

8. In general, as age increases, the amount of water per pound of body weight (increases or decreases).

9. Excluding adipose tissue, approximately (55% or 85%) of body weight is water.

10. The term (fluid balance or fluid compartments) means the volumes of ICF, IF, plasma, and the total volume of water in the body all remain relatively constant.

▸ If you have had difficulty with this section, review pages 474-475. ◂

MECHANISMS THAT MAINTAIN FLUID BALANCE

Circle the correct choice.

11. Which one of the following is *not* an anion?

    a. Chloride
    b. Bicarbonate
    c. Sodium
    d. Many proteins

12. Which one of the following is *not* a cation?

    a. Sodium
    b. Potassium
    c. Calcium
    d. Magnesium
    e. All of the above are cations

13. The most abundant cation in the blood plasma is:

    a. Sodium
    b. Chloride
    c. Protein
    d. Calcium
    e. Magnesium

14. The smallest amount of water comes from:

    a. Water in foods that are eaten
    b. Ingested liquids
    c. Water formed from catabolism
    d. None of the above is correct

15. The greatest amount of water lost from the body is from the:

    a. Lungs
    b. Skin by diffusion
    c. Skin by sweat
    d. Feces
    e. Kidneys

16. Which one of the following is *not* a major factor that influences extracellular and intracellular fluid volumes?

    a. The concentration of electrolytes in the extracellular fluid
    b. The capillary blood pressure
    c. The concentration of proteins in blood
    d. All of the above are important factors

17. The type of fluid output that changes the most is:

    a. Water loss in the feces
    b. Water loss across the skin
    c. Water loss via the lungs
    d. Water loss in the urine
    e. None of the above is correct

18. The chief regulators of sodium within the body are the:

    a. Lungs
    b. Sweat glands
    c. Kidneys
    d. Large intestine
    e. None of the above is correct

19. Which of the following is *not* correct?

   a. Fluid output must equal fluid intake.
   b. ADH controls salt reabsorption in the kidney.
   c. Water follows sodium.
   d. Renal tubule regulation of salt and water is the most important factor in determining urine volume.
   e. All of the above are correct.

20. Diuretics work on all but which one of the following?

   a. Proximal tubule
   b. Loop of Henle
   c. Distal tubule

   d. Collecting ducts
   e. Diuretics work on all of the above

21. Of all the sodium-containing secretions, the one with the largest volume is:

   a. Saliva
   b. Gastric secretions
   c. Bile

   d. Pancreatic juice
   e. Intestinal secretions

22. The higher the capillary blood pressure, the _____ the amount of interstitial fluid.

   a. Smaller
   b. Larger
   c. There is no relationship between capillary blood pressure and volume of interstitial fluid

23. An increase in capillary blood pressure will lead to _____ in blood volume.

   a. An increase
   b. A decrease

   c. No change
   d. None of the above is correct

24. Which one of the fluid compartments varies the most in volume?

   a. Intracellular
   b. Interstitial

   c. Extracellular
   d. Plasma

*If the following statements are true, insert **T** in the answer blanks. If any of the statements are false, circle the incorrect word(s) and write the correct word in the answer blank.*

_____ 25. The three sources of fluid intake are: the liquids we drink, the foods we eat, and water formed by the anabolism of foods.
_____ 26. The body maintains fluid balance mainly by changing the volume of urine excreted to match changes in the volume of fluid intake.
_____ 27. Some output of fluid will occur as long as life continues.
_____ 28. Glucose is an example of an electrolyte.
_____ 29. Where sodium goes, water soon follows.
_____ 30. Excess aldosterone leads to hypovolemia.
_____ 31. Diuretics have their effect on glomerular function.
_____ 32. Typical daily intake and output totals should be approximately 1200 ml.
_____ 33. Bile is a sodium-containing internal secretion.
_____ 34. The average daily diet contains about 500 mEg of sodium.

▶ If you have had difficulty with this section, review pages 474-482. ◀

FLUID IMBALANCES

Fill in the blanks.

(35)_____ is the fluid imbalance seen most often. In this condition, interstitial fluid volume

(36) _____ first, but eventually, if treatment has not been given, intracellular fluid and plasma

volumes (37) _____. (38) _____ can also occur, but is much less common. Giving

(39) _____ too rapidly or in too large amounts can put too heavy a burden on the (40)

_____.

▶ If you have had difficulty with this section, review page 482. ◀

APPLYING WHAT YOU KNOW

41. Mrs. Titus was asked to keep an accurate record of her fluid intake and output. She was concerned because the two did not balance. What is a possible explanation for this?

42. Nurse Briker was caring for a patient who was receiving diuretics. What special nursing implications should be followed for patients on this therapy?

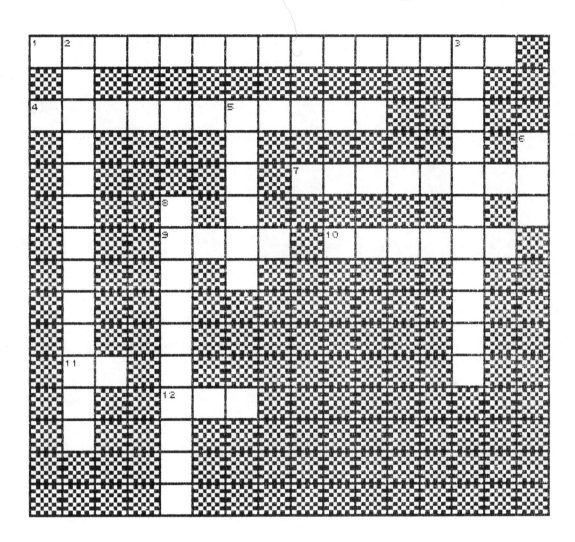

ACROSS

1. Organic substances that don't dissociate in solution
4. Total volume of body fluids less than normal
7. "Causing urine"
9. Dissociated particles of an electrolyte that carry an electrical charge
10. Positively charged ion
11. A subdivision of extracellular fluid (abbrev.)
12. Fluid inside cells (abbrev.)

DOWN

2. Total volume of body fluids greater than normal
3. Compound that dissociates in solution into ions
5. Negatively charged ions
6. Fluid outside cells (abbrev.)
8. To break up

CHAPTER 20

Acid-Base Balance

It has been established in previous chapters that an equilibrium between intracellular and extracellular fluid volume must exist for homeostasis. Equally important to homeostasis is the chemical acid-base balance of the body fluids. The degree of acidity or alkalinity of a body fluid is expressed in pH value. The neutral point, where a fluid would be neither acid nor alkaline, is pH 7. Increasing acidity is expressed as less than 7, and increasing alkalinity as greater than 7. Examples of body fluids that are acidic are gastric juice (1.6) and urine (6.0). Blood, on the other hand, is considered alkaline with a pH of 7.45.

Buffers are substances that prevent a sharp change in the pH of a fluid when an acid or base is added to it. They are one of several mechanisms that are constantly monitoring the pH of fluids in the body. If, for any reason, these mechanisms do not function properly, a pH imbalance occurs. These two kinds of imbalances are known as alkalosis and acidosis.

Maintaining the acid-base balance of body fluids is a matter of vital importance. If this balance varies even slightly, necessary chemical and cellular reactions cannot occur. Your review of this chapter is necessary to understand the delicate fluid balance necessary to survival.

TOPICS FOR REVIEW

Before progressing to Chapter 21 you should have an understanding of the pH of body fluids and the mechanisms that control the pH of these fluids in the body. Your study should conclude with a review of the metabolic and respiratory types of pH imbalances.

pH OF BODY

Write the letter of the correct term on the blank next to the appropriate statement.

(a) Acid   (b) Base

_____ 1. Lower concentration of hydrogen ions than hydroxide ions
_____ 2. Higher concentration of hydrogen ions than hydroxide ions
_____ 3. Gastric juice
_____ 4. Saliva
_____ 5. Arterial blood
_____ 6. Venous blood
_____ 7. Baking soda
_____ 8. Milk
_____ 9. Ammonia
_____ 10. Egg white

▶ If you have had difficulty with this section, review pages 486-487. ◀

MECHANISMS THAT CONTROL pH OF BODY FLUIDS

Circle the correct choice.

11. When carbon dioxide enters the blood it reacts with the enzyme carbonic anhydrase to form:

    a. Sodium bicarbonate
    b. Water and carbon dioxide
    c. Ammonium chloride

    d. Bicarbonate ion
    e. Carbonic acid

12. The lungs remove _____ liters of carbonic acid each day.

    a. 10.0
    b. 15.0
    c. 20.0

    d. 25.0
    e. 30.0

13. When a buffer reacts with a strong acid it changes the strong acid to a:

    a. Weak acid
    b. Strong base
    c. Weak base

    d. Water
    e. None of the above is correct

14. Which one of the following is *not* a change in the blood that results from the buffering of fixed acids in tissue capillaries?

    a. The amount of carbonic acid increases slightly.
    b. The amount of bicarbonate in blood decreases.
    c. The hydrogen ion concentration of blood increases slightly.
    d. The blood pH decreases slightly.
    e. All of the above are changes that result from the buffering of nonvolatile acids in tissue capillaries.

15. The most abundant acid in the body is:

    a. HCL
    b. Lactic acid
    c. Carbonic acid

    d. Acetic acid
    e. Sulfuric acid

16. The normal ratio of sodium bicarbonate to carbonic acid in arterial blood is:

    a. 5:1
    b. 10:1
    c. 15:1

    d. 20:1
    e. None of the above is correct

17. Which of the following would *not* be a consequence of holding your breath?

    a. The amount of carbonic acid in the blood would increase.
    b. The blood pH would decrease.
    c. The body would develop an alkalosis.
    d. No carbon dioxide could leave the body.

18. The most effective regulators of blood pH are:

a. The lungs
b. The kidneys

c Buffers
d. None of the above

19. The pH of the urine may be as low as:

a. 1.6
b. 2.5
c 3.2

d. 4.8
e. 7.4

20. In the distal tubule cells the product of the reaction aided by carbonic anhydrase is:

a. Water
b. Carbon dioxide
c. Water and carbon dioxide

d. Hydrogen ions
e. Carbonic acid

21. In the distal tubule, _____ leaves the tubule cells and enters the blood capillaries.

a. Carbon dioxide
b. Water
c. HCO$_3$

d. NaH$_2$PO$_4$
e. NaHCO$_3$

Mark T in the answer blank if the statement is true. If the statement is false, circle the incorrect word(s) and correct the statement on the answer blank.

_____ 22. The body has three mechanisms for regulating the pH of its fluids. They are the heart mechanism, the respiratory mechanism, and the urinary mechanism.

_____ 23. Buffers consist of two kinds of substances and are therefore often called duobuffers.

_____ 24. Oranges and grapefruit are not acid forming when metabolized.

_____ 25. Some athletes have adopted a technique called bicarbonate loading, ingesting large amounts of sodium bicarbonate (NaHCO$_3$) to counteract the effects of lactic acid buildup.

_____ 26. Anything that causes an excessive increase in respiration will in time produce acidosis.

_____ 27. Venous blood has a higher pH than arterial blood.

_____ 28. More acids than bases are usually excreted by the kidneys because more acids than bases usually enter the blood.

_____ 29. Blood levels of sodium bicarbonate can be regulated by the lungs.

_____ 30. Blood levels of carbonic acid can be regulated by the kidneys.

► If you have had difficulty with this section, review pages 486-494. ◄

METABOLIC AND RESPIRATORY DISTURBANCES

Write the letter of the correct term on the blank next to the appropriate definition.

a. Metabolic acidosis
b. Metabolic alkalosis
c. Respiratory acidosis
d. Respiratory alkalosis
e. Vomiting

f. Normal saline
g. Uncompensated metabolic acidosis
h. Hyperventilation
i. HCl loss
j. Ipecac

_____31. Emesis
_____32. Result of untreated diabetes
_____33. Chloride containing solution
_____34. Bicarbonate deficit
_____35. Occurs during emesis
_____36. Bicarbonate excess
_____37. Rapid breathing
_____38. Carbonic acid excess
_____39. Carbonic acid deficit
_____40. Emetic

▶ If you have had difficulty with this section, review pages 491. ◀

APPLYING WHAT YOU KNOW

41. Cara was pregnant and was experiencing repeated vomiting episodes for several days. Her doctor became concerned, admitted her to the hospital, and began intravenous administrations of normal saline. How will this help Cara?

42. Holly had a minor bladder infection. She had heard that this is often the result of the urine being less acidic than necessary, and that she should drink cranberry juice to correct the acid problem. She had no cranberry juice, so she decided to substitute orange juice. What was wrong with this substitution?

43. Mr. Cameron has frequent bouts of hyperacidity of the stomach. Which will assist in neutralizing the acid more promptly; milk or milk of magnesia?

44. WORD FIND

Can you find the terms from this chapter listed below in the box of letters? Words may be spelled top to bottom, bottom to top, right to left, left to right, or diagonally.

```
Q G J F M B F N A K N H A C J L J F N W
W K D I U R E T I C Y Q Y I W Y I C O V
D B X Z X E C N A L A B D I U L F Z I M
E E T S H J A L D O S T E R O N E Z T G
H E I R N S C F U V X F W K P Z B X A Y
Y L Q E I O L D R O J T M D E R Q H R M
D E J L K S I O W S B X D S E P O L D X
R C A Y U R M T O U U Q K N S M A X Y R
A T V A F B O D A O E Z Z I E H R X H Z
T R N K J H I A G C W I J O D D U J R L
I O D H E U A Z B O H N S F J N L K E L
O L X T M N C N U D Y T D B T B E P V I
N Y U E I Q Z T W D A A X O M I D Y O M
J T T O J S P H B S U K T W I A E I S S
V E N W F U Z H I J O E S I A N M N P B
S S B C T L D S Q X Q L R C Q T A Q W E
C F J Q W C U R H C G P I A Y L E J X R
W F Y B E K E D R V S L H D I C F R C H
O R N I A Y A C U S Q L T M R S T Y Z K
L N O N E L E C T R O L Y T E S M S V J
```

LIST OF WORDS

FLUID BALANCE	ALDOSTERONE	INTAKE
OUTPUT	KIDNEYS	WATER
HOMEOSTASIS	ELECTROLYTES	THIRST
SODIUM	DIURETIC	EDEMA
ADH	DEHYDRATION	OVERHYDRATION
CATIONS	ANIONS	NONELECTROLYTES

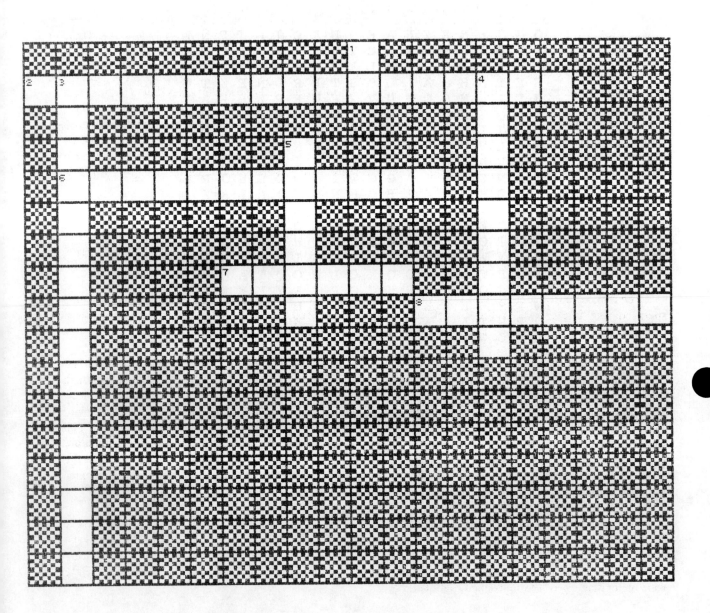

ACROSS

2. An enzyme found in red blood cells (two words)
6. Substance with a pH lower than 7.0 (two words)
7. Vomitus
8. Acid-base imbalance

DOWN

1. Way to express the acidity or alkalinity of a substance
3. Substance with a pH higher than 7.0 (two words)
4. Serious complication of vomiting
5. Prevents a sharp change in the pH of fluids

CHAPTER 21

The Reproductive Systems

The reproductive system consists of those organs that participate in perpetuating the species. It is a unique body system in that its organs differ between the two sexes, and yet the goal of creating a new being is the same. Of interest also is the fact that this system is the only one not necessary to the survival of the individual, and yet survival of the species depends on the proper functioning of the reproductive organs. The male reproductive system is divided into the external genitals: the testes, the duct system, and accessory glands. The testes, or gonads, are considered essential organs because they produce the sex cells, sperm, which join with the female sex cells, ova, to form a new human being. They also secrete the male sex hormone, testosterone, which is responsible for the physical transformation of a boy to a man.

Sperm are formed in the testes by the seminiferous tubules. From there they enter a long narrow duct, the epididymis. They continue onward through the vas deferens into the ejaculatory duct, down the urethra, and out of the body. Throughout this journey, various glands secrete substances that add motility to the sperm and create a chemical environment conducive to reproduction.

The female reproductive system is truly extraordinary and diverse. It produces ova, receives the penis and sperm during intercourse, is the site of conception, houses and nourishes the embryo during prenatal development, and nourishes the infant after birth.

Because of its diversity, the physiology of the female is generally considered to be more complex than that of the male. Much of the activity of this system revolves around the menstrual cycle and the monthly preparation that the female undergoes for a possible pregnancy.

The organs of this system are divided into essential organs and accessory organs of reproduction. The essential organs of the female are the ovaries. Just as with the male, the essential organs of the female are referred to as the gonads. The gonads of both sexes produce the sex cells. In the male, the gonads produce the sperm and in the female they produce the ova. The gonads are also responsible for producing the hormones in each sex necessary for the appearance of the secondary sex characteristics.

The menstrual cycle of the female typically covers a period of 28 days. Each cycle consists of three phases: the menstrual period, the postmenstrual phase, and the premenstrual phase. Changes in the blood levels of the hormones that are responsible for the menstrual cycle also cause physical and emotional changes in the female. A knowledge of these phenomena and this system, in both the male and the female, are necessary to complete your understanding of the reproductive system.

TOPICS FOR REVIEW

Before progressing to Chapter 22 you should familiarize yourself with the structure and function of the organs of the male and female reproductive systems. Your review should include emphasis on the gross and microscopic structure of the testes and the production of sperm and testosterone. Your study should continue by tracing the pathway of a sperm cell from formation to expulsion from the body.

You should then familiarize yourself with the structure and function of the organs of the female reproductive system. Your review should include emphasis on the development of a mature ova from ovarian follicles, and should additionally concentrate on the phases and occurrences in a typical 28-day menstrual cycle. Finally, a review of the common disorders occurring in both male and female reproducive systems is necessary to complete the study of this chapter.

STRUCTURAL PLAN

Match the term on the left with the proper selection on the right.

Group A

_____ 1. Testes   a. Fertilized ovum
_____ 2. Spermatozoa   b. Accessory organ
_____ 3. Ova   c. Male sex cell
_____ 4. Penis   d. Gonads
_____ 5. Zygote   e. Gamete

Group B

_____ 6. Testes   a. Cowper's gland
_____ 7. Bulbourethral   b. Corpus cavernosum
_____ 8. Asexual   c. Essential organ
_____ 9. Erectile tissue   d. Single parent
_____ 10. Prostate   e. Accessory organ

▸ If you have had difficulty with this section, review pages 498-499. ◂

TESTES

Circle the correct choice.

11. The testes are surrounded by a tough membrane called:

a. Ductus deferens   c. Septum
b. Tunica albuginea   d. Seminiferous membrane

12. The _____ lie near the septa that separate the lobules.

a. Ductus deferens   c. Interstitial cells
b. Sperm   d. Nerves

13. Sperm are found in the walls of the _____ .

a. Seminiferous tubule   c. Septum
b. Interstitial cells   d. Blood vessels

14. The scrotum provides an environment approximately _____ for the testes.

    a. The same as body temperature
    b. 5 degrees warmer than body temperature
    c. 3 degrees warmer than body temperature
    d. 3 degrees cooler than body temperature

15. The structures that produces testosterone is (are) the:

    a. Seminiferous tubules
    b. Prostate gland
    c. Bulbourethral gland

    d. Pituitary gland
    e. Interstitial cells

16. The part of the sperm that contains genetic information that will be inherited is the:

    a. Tail
    b. Neck
    c. Middle piece

    d. Head
    e. Acrosome

17. Which one of the following is *not* a function of testosterone?

    a. It causes a deepening of the voice.
    b. It promotes the development of the male accessory glands.
    c. It has a stimulatory effect on protein catabolism.
    d. It causes greater muscular development and strength.

18. Sperm production is called:

    a. Spermatogonia
    b. Spermatids

    c. Spermatogenesis
    d. Spermatocyte

19. The section of the sperm that contains enzymes that enable it to break down the covering of the ovum and permit entry should contact occur is the:

    a. Acrosome
    b. Midpiece

    c. Tail
    d. Stem

Fill in the blanks.

The (20) _____ are the gonads of the male. From puberty on, the seminiferous tubules are continuously forming (21) _____. Any of these cells may join with the female sex cell, the (22) _____ to become a new human being.

Another function of the testes is to secrete the male hormone (23) _____, that transforms a boy to a man. This hormone is secreted by the (24) _____ of the testes. A good way to remember testosterone's functions is to think of it as "the (25) _____ hormone" and "the (26) _____ hormone."

► If you have had difficulty with this section, review pages 498-503. ◄

DUCTS
ACCESSORY MALE REPRODUCTIVE GLANDS

Choose the correct term and write its letter in the space next to the appropriate definition below.

a. Epididymis
b. Vas deferens
c. Ejaculatory duct
d. Prepuce
e. Seminal vesicles

f. Prostate gland
g. Cowper's gland
h. Corpus spongiosum
i. Semen
j. Scrotum

_____ 27. Continuation of ducts that start in epididymis
_____ 28. Erectile tissue
_____ 29. Also known as bulbourethral
_____ 30. Narrow tube that lies along the top and behind the testes
_____ 31. Doughnut-shaped gland beneath bladder
_____ 32. Continuation of vas deferens
_____ 33. Mixture of sperm and secretions of accessory sex glands
_____ 34. Contributes 60% of the seminal fluid volume
_____ 35. Removed during circumcision
_____ 36. External genitalia

► If you have had difficulty with this section, review pages 498-505. ◄

DISORDERS OF THE MALE REPRODUCTIVE SYSTEM

Fill in the blanks.

37. Decreased sperm production is called _____.

38. Testes normally descend into the scrotum about _____ before birth.

39. If a baby is born with undescended testes, a condition called _____ results.

40. A common noncancerous condition of the prostate in older men is known as _____

_____ _____.

41. _____ is a condition in which the foreskin fits so tightly over the glans that it cannot retract.

42. Failure to achieve an erection of the penis is called _____.

43. An accumulation of fluid in the scrotum is known as a _____.

44. An _____ _____ results when the intestines push through the weak area of the abdominal wall that separates the abdominopelvic cavity from the scrotum.

45. The PSA test is a screening test for cancer of the _____.

▶ If you have had difficulty with this section, review pages 505-506. ◀

STRUCTURAL PLAN

Match the term on the left with the proper selection on the right.

_____46. Ovaries
_____47. Vagina
_____48. Bartholin
_____49. Vulva
_____50. Ova

a. Genitals
b. Accessory sex gland
c. Accessory duct
d. Gonads
e. Sex cell

Write the letter of the correct description in the blank next to the appropriate structure.

(a) External structure

(b) Internal structure

_____51. Mons pubis
_____52. Vagina
_____53. Labia majora
_____54. Uterine tubes
_____55. Vestibule
_____56. Clitoris
_____57. Labia minora
_____58. Ovaries

▶ If you have had difficulty with this section, review pages 507 and 512. ◀

OVARIES

Fill in the blanks.

The ovaries are the (59) _____ of the female. They have two main functions. The first is the production of the female sex cell. This process is called (60) _____. The specialized type of cell division that occurs during sexual cell reproduction is known as (61) _____. The ovum is the body's largest cell and has (62) _____ the number of chromosomes found in other body cells. At the time of (63) _____, the sex cells from both parents fuse and (64) _____ chromosomes are united.

The second major function of the ovaries is to secrete the sex hormones (65) _____ and (66) _____. Estrogen is the sex hormone that causes the development and maintenance of the female (67) _____. Progesterone acts with estrogen to help initiate the (68) _____ in girls entering (69) _____.

▶ If you have had difficulty with this section, review pages 507-509. ◀

FEMALE REPRODUCTIVE DUCTS

Write the letter of the correct structure in the blank next to the appropriate definition.

(a) Uterine tubes   (b) Uterus   (c) Vagina

_____70. Ectopic pregnancy
_____71. Lining known as endometrium
_____72. Terminal end of birth canal
_____73. Site of menstruation
_____74. Approximately 4 inches in length
_____75. Consists of body, fundus, and cervix
_____76. Site of fertilization
_____77. Also known as oviduct
_____78. Entrance way for sperm

▶ If you have had difficulty with this section, review pages 509-511. ◀

ACCESSORY FEMALE
REPRODUCTIVE GLANDS
EXTERNAL GENITALS OF THE FEMALE

Match the term on the left with the proper selection on the right.

Group A

_____79. Bartholin's gland
_____80. Breasts
_____81. Alveoli
_____82. Lactiferous ducts
_____83. Areola

    a. Colored area around nipple
    b. Grapelike clusters of milk-secreting cells
    c. Drain alveoli
    d. Secretes lubricating fluid
    e. Primarily fat tissue

Group B

_____84. Mons pubis
_____85. Labia majora
_____86. Clitoris
_____87. Vestibule
_____88. Episiotomy

    a. "Large lips"
    b. Area between labia minora
    c. Surgical procedure
    d. Composed of erectile tissue
    e. Pad of fat over the symphysis pubis

▶ If you have had difficulty with this section, review pages 511-513. ◀

MENSTRUAL CYCLE

*If the following statement is true, insert **T** in the answer blank. If the statement is false, circle the incorrect word(s) and insert the correct word(s) in the answer blank.*

_____89. Climacteric is the scientific name for the beginning of the menses.
_____90. As a general rule, several ovum mature each month during the 30-40 years that a woman has menstrual periods.
_____91. Ovulation occurs 28 days before the next menstrual period begins.
_____92. The first day of ovulation is considered the first day of the cycle.
_____93. A woman's fertile period lasts only a few days out of each month.
_____94. The control of the menstrual cycle lies in the posterior pituitary gland.

Write the letter of the correct hormone in the blank next to the appropriate description.

(a) FSH   (b) LH

_____95. Ovulating hormone
_____96. Secreted during first days of menstrual cycle
_____97. Secreted after estrogen level of blood increases
_____98. Causes final maturation of follicle and ovum
_____99. Birth control pills suppress this one

▶ If you have had difficulty with this section, review pages 513-515. ◀

DISORDERS OF THE FEMALE REPRODUCTIVE SYSTEM

Choose the correct response.

a. Toxic shock syndrome
b. Dysmenorrhea
c. Exogenous infections
d. DUB
e. Myoma
f. Vaginitis

g. Sexually transmitted diseases (STDs)
h. Oophorectomy
i. Fibrocystic disease
j. Pap smear
k. Genital herpes
l. Trichomoniasis

_____100. Often occurs from STDs or from a "yeast infection"
_____101. Benign tumor of smooth muscle and fibrous connective tissue
_____102. Most often occurs in women who use super-absorbent tampons to absorb the menstrual flow
_____103. Removal of ovaries
_____104. Benign lumps in one or both breasts
_____105. Venereal diseases
_____106. Results from pathogenic organisms transmitted from another person; e.g., STD
_____107. Painful menstruation
_____108. Asymptomatic in most women and nearly all men
_____109. Results from a hormonal imbalance rather than from an infection or disease condition
_____110. Screening test for cervical cancer
_____111. Causes blisters on the skin of the genitals. The blisters may disappear temporarily, but reoccur, especially as a result of stress.

> ▸ If you have had difficulty with this section, review pages 516-520. ◂

APPLYING WHAT YOU KNOW

112. Mr. Belinki is going into the hospital for the surgical removal of his testes. As a result of this surgery, will Mr. Belinki be sterile or impotent?

113. When baby Gaylor was born, the pediatrician discovered that his left testicle had not descended into the scrotum. If this situation is not corrected soon might baby Gaylor be sterile or impotent?

114. Marcia contracted gonorrhea. By the time she made an appointment to see her doctor, it had spread to her abdominal organs. How is this possible when gonorrhea is a disease of the reproductive system?

115. Mrs. Harlan was having a bilateral oophorectomy. Is this a sterilization procedure? Will she experience menopause?

116. Ms. Comstock had a total hysterectomy. Will she experience menopause?

117. WORD FIND

Can you find the terms from this chapter listed below in the box of letters? Words may be spelled top to bottom, bottom to top, right to left, left to right, or diagonally.

```
L K B W M H W K K L R Q Q P C W V U X X
G K P X U C U U J H Y Q X Z T B D L M M
A B I Y T I O V I D U C T S C K R R C U
C H A Y O M L P G K C F C O W P E R S M
R L V W R F Q I M X B M H Z T G Z O R S
O G X T C L J T Q A M V E A H L L G T I
S S S S H P I C M O R H I B M F O X D
O N S E M I N I F E R O U S O S P D P I
M E I Q E N D O M E T R I U M S Z F S H
E R J K I F K U L J P P J H M R I Z I C
D E E G J Q O Q S P E R M A T I D S M R
E F W S L E S T R O G E N K E S T Y Y O
S E J E L S Q Z Q J J R I V Y P Y H D T
Q D A I C G X E L Y C M W R J E F V I P
W S P R O S T A T E C T O M Y R S A D Y
R A Q A C I P B F X F M N X I M C G I R
I V U V C E E E P V F E L Z T U A I P C
P M M O V R N Q L Y W U B U T B B N E E
E Q H A B X I N D G D S P I C D O A G O
L W Z X E Z S P R E G N A N C Y T O J S
```

LIST OF WORDS

SPERM

CRYPTORCHIDISM

ACROSOME

COWPERS

OVARIES

PREGNANCY

SEMINIFEROUS

MEIOSIS

EPIDIDYMIS

PENIS

ESTROGEN

ENDOMETRIUM

SCROTUM

SPERMATIDS

VASDEFERENS

PROSTATECTOMY

OVIDUCTS

VAGINA

DID YOU KNOW?

The ovaries contain approximately 500,000 ova cells, but only 400+ will mature and be capable of being fertilized.

The testes produce approximately 50 million sperm per day. Every 2 months they produce enough cells to populate the entire earth.

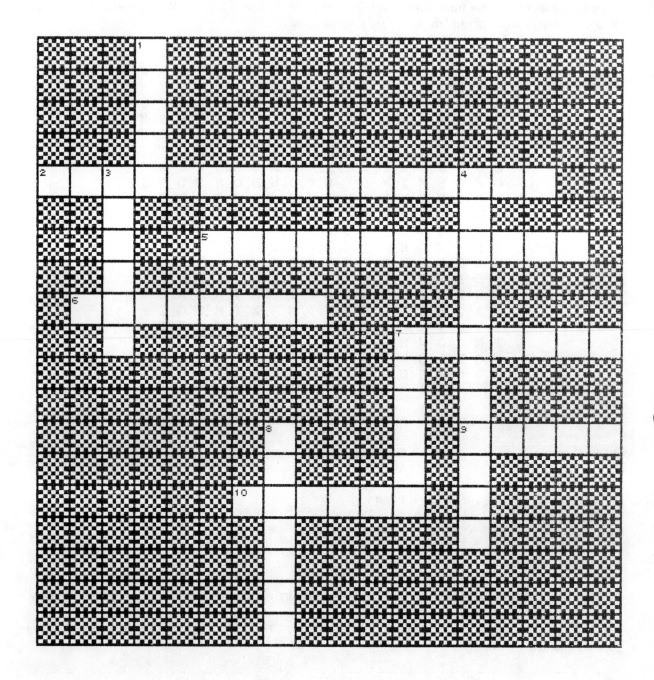

ACROSS

2. The sac that contains a mature ovum
5. Male sex hormone
6. Female erectile tissue
7. Sex cells
9. Male reproductive fluid
10. Menstrual period

DOWN

1. External genitalia
3. Colored area around nipple
4. Surgical removal of foreskin
7. Essential organs of reproduction
8. Foreskin

MALE REPRODUCTIVE ORGANS

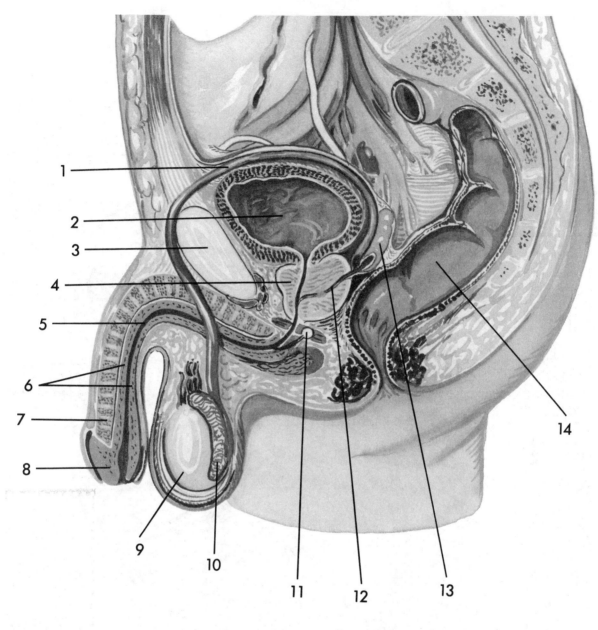

1. _____

2. _____

3. _____

4. _____

5. _____

6. _____

7. _____

8. _____

9. _____

10. _____

11. _____

12. _____

13. _____

14. _____

TUBULES OF TESTIS AND EPIDIDYMIS

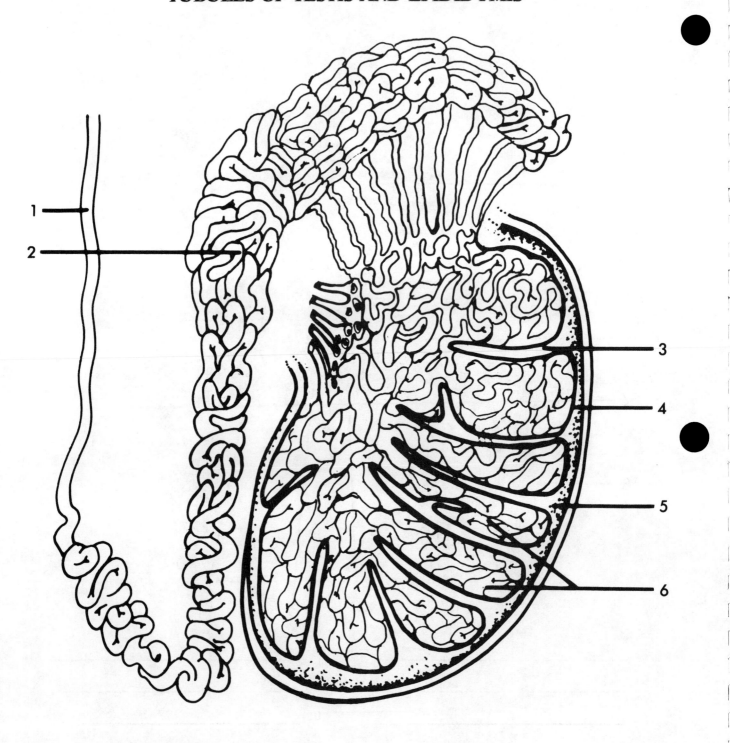

1. _____   4. _____

2. _____   5. _____

3. _____   6. _____

VULVA

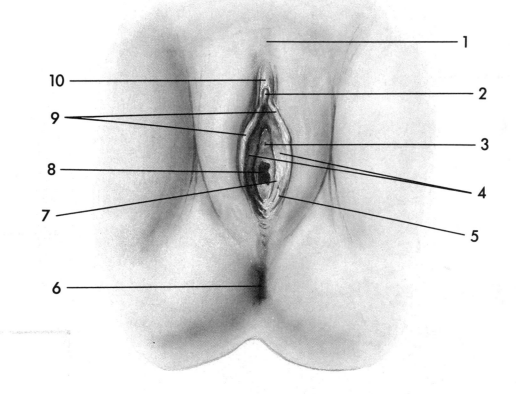

1.

2.

3.

4.

5.

6.

7.

8.

9.

10.

BREAST

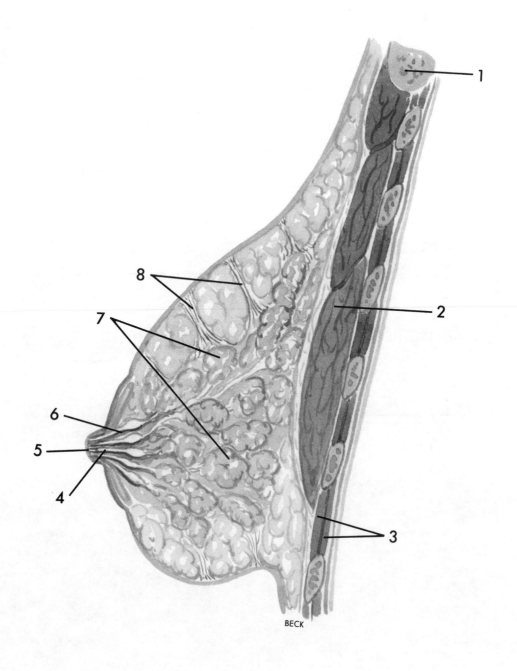

1 —

2 —

3

4

5

6

7

8

BECK

1. _____   5. _____

2. _____   6. _____

3. _____   7. _____

4. _____   8. _____

FEMALE PELVIS

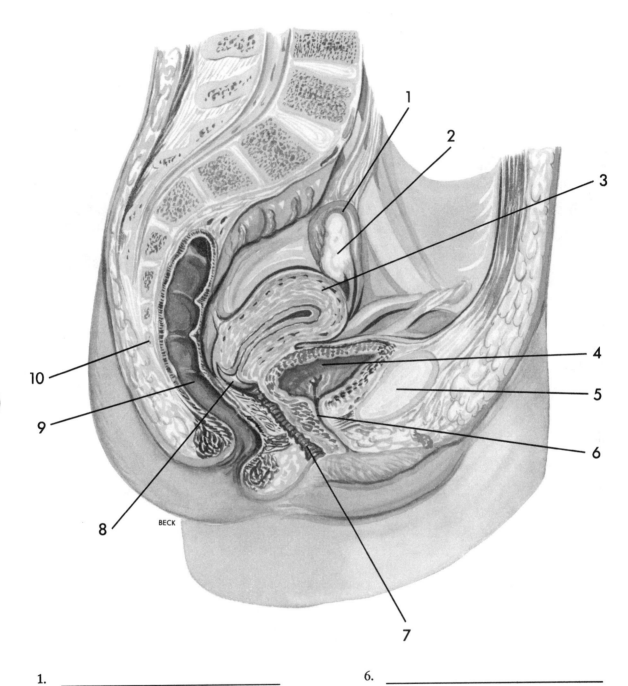

BECK

1. _____   6. _____

2. _____   7. _____

3. _____   8. _____

4. _____   9. _____

5. _____   10. _____

221

UTERUS AND ADJACENT STRUCTURES

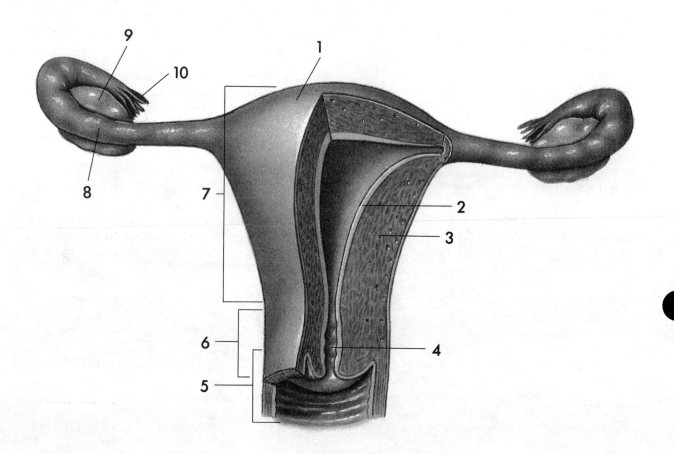

1. _____

2. _____

3. _____

4. _____

5. _____

6. _____

7. _____

8. _____

9. _____

10. _____

CHAPTER 22

Growth and Development

Millions of fragile microscopic sperm swim against numerous obstacles to reach the ova and create a new life. At birth, the newborn will fill his lungs with air and cry lustily, signaling to the world that he is ready to begin the cycle of life. This cycle will be marked by ongoing changes, periodic physical growth, and continuous development.

This chapter reviews the more significant events that occur in the normal growth and development of an individual from conception to death. Realizing that each individual is unique, we nonetheless can discover amid all the complexities of humanity some constants that are understandable and predictable.

A knowledge of human growth and development is essential in understanding the commonalities that influence individuals as they pass through the cycle of life.

TOPICS FOR REVIEW

Before progressing to Chapter 23 you should have an understanding of the concept of development as a biological process. You should familiarize yourself with the major developmental changes from conception through older adulthood. Finally, your study should conclude with a review of the effects of aging on the body systems. The disorders of pregnancy should be emphasized as you review the chapter.

PRENATAL PERIOD

Fill in the blanks.

The prenatal stage of development begins at the time of (1) _____ and continues until (2)

_____ . The science of the development of an individual before birth is called (3) _____ .

Fertilization takes place in the outer third of the (4) _____ . The fertilized ovum or (5)

_____ begins to divide and in approximately 3 days forms a solid mass called a (6)

_____ . By the time it enters the uterus, it is a hollow ball of cells called a (7) _____ .

As it continues to develop, it forms a structure with two cavities. The (8) _____ _____

will become a fluid-filled sac for the embryo. The (9) _____ will develop into an important fetal

membrane in the (10) _____ .

Choose the correct term and write its letter in the space next to the appropriate definition below.

a. Laparoscope
b. Gestation
c. Antenatal
d. Histogenesis
e. C-section

f. Endoderm
g. In vitro
h. Parturition
i. Embryonic phase
j. Ultrasonogram

_____11. "Within a glass"
_____12. Inside germ layer
_____13. Before birth
_____14. Length of pregnancy
_____15. Optical viewing tube
_____16. Process of birth
_____17. Surgical procedure in which a newborn is delivered through an incision in the abdomen and uterine wall
_____18. Study of how the primary germ layers develop into many different kinds of tissues
_____19. Fertilization until the end of the eighth week of gestation
_____20. Monitors progress of developing fetus

▶ If you have had difficulty with this section, review pages 528-539. ◀

DISORDERS OF PREGNANCY

*Mark **T** in the answer blank if the statement is true. If the statement is false, circle the incorrect word(s) and correct the statement in the answer blank.*

_____21. Many offspring are lost before implantation occurs, often for unknown reasons.
_____22. The most common type of ectopic pregnancy is a tubal pregnancy.
_____23. If the placenta grows too closely to the cervical opening a condition called abruptio placentae results.
_____24. Separation of the placenta from the uterine wall in a pregnancy of 20 weeks or more is known as placenta previa.
_____25. Toxemia of pregnancy is also known as puerperal fever.
_____26. After 20 weeks, delivery of a lifeless infant is termed a miscarriage.
_____27. Acquired birth defects result from agents called teratogens that disrupt normal histogenesis and organogenesis.

▶ If you have had difficulty with this section, review pages 538-540. ◀

POSTNATAL PERIOD

Circle the correct choice.

28. During the postnatal period:

a. The head becomes proportionately smaller
b. The relationship of the face to skull is reduced
c. The legs become proportionately longer
d. The trunk becomes proportionately shorter
e. All of the above take place during the postnatal period

29. The period of infancy starts at birth and lasts about:

a. 4 weeks
b. 4 months
c. 10 weeks

d. 12 months
e. 18 months

30. The lumbar curvature of the spine appears _____ months after birth.

a. 1-10
b. 5-8
c. 8-12

d. 11-15
e. 12-18

31. During the first 4 months the birth weight will:

a. Double
b. Triple

c. Quadruple
d. None of the above is correct

32. At the end of the first year the weight of the baby will have:

a. Doubled
b. Tripled

c. Quadrupled
d. None of the above is correct

33. The infant is capable of following a moving object with its eyes at:

a. 2 days
b. 2 weeks
c. 2 months

d. 4 months
e. 10 months

34. The infant can lift its head and raise its chest at:

a. 2 months
b. 3 months

c. 4 months
d. 10 months

35. The infant can crawl at:

a. 2 months
b. 3 months
c. 4 months

d. 10 months
e. 12 months

36. The infant can stand alone at:

a. 2 months
b. 3 months
c. 4 months

d. 10 months
e. 12 months

37. The permanent teeth, with the exception of the third molar, have all erupted by age _____ years.

a. 6
b. 8
c. 12

d. 14
e. None of the above is correct

38. Puberty starts at age _____ years in boys:

a. 10-13
b. 12-14

c. 14-16
d. None of the above is correct

39. Most girls begin breast development at about age:

a. 8
b. 9
c. 10

d. 11
e. 12

40. The growth spurt is generally complete by age _____ in males:

a. 14
b. 15

c. 16
d. 18

41. An average age at which girls begin to menstruate is _____ years.

a. 10-12
b. 11-12
c. 12-13

d. 13-14
e. 14-15

42. The first sign of puberty in boys is:

a. Facial hair
b. Increased muscle mass
c. Pubic hair

d. Deepening of the voice
e. Increased testicular enlargement

Write the letter of the correct word in the blank next to the appropriate definition.

a. Neonatology
b. Neonatal
c. Adolescence
d. Deciduous
e. Puberty

f. Postnatal
g. Infancy
h. Childhood
i. Senescence

_____ 43. Begins at birth and lasts until death
_____ 44. Concerned with the diagnosis and treatment of disorders of the newborn
_____ 45. Teenage years
_____ 46. From the end of infancy to puberty
_____ 47. Baby teeth
_____ 48. First 4 weeks of infancy
_____ 49. Secondary sexual characteristics occur
_____ 50. Begins at birth and lasts about 18 months
_____ 51. Old age

▸ If you have had difficulty with this section, review pages 541-544. ◂

EFFECTS OF AGING

Fill in the blanks.

52. Old bones develop indistinct and shaggy margins with spurs; a process called _____.

53. A degenerative joint disease common in the aged is _____.

54. The number of _____ units in the kidney decreases by almost 50% between the ages of 30 and 75.

55. In old age, respiratory efficiency decreases, and a condition known as _____ _____ results.

56. Fatty deposits accumulate in blood vessels as we age, and the result is _____ which narrows the passageway for the flow of blood.

57. Hardening of the arteries or _____ occurs during the aging process.

58. Another term for high blood pressure is _____.

59. Hardening of the lens is _____.

60. If the lens becomes cloudy and impairs vision, it is called a _____.

61. _____ causes an increase in the pressure within the eyeball and may result in blindness.

▸ If you have had difficulty with this section, review pages 544-546. ◂

Unscramble the words.

62. **ANNFCYI**

63. **NAALTTSOP**

64. **OGSSNEGRAONEI**

65. **GTEYZO**

66. **HDOOLHCID**

The secret is in the bag!

1ST PRIZE

Take the circled letters, unscramble them, and fill in the statement.

The secret to Farmer Brown's prize pumpkin crop.

67.

APPLYING WHAT YOU KNOW

68. Heather's mother told the pediatrician during her 1-year visit that she had tripled her birth weight, was crawling actively, and could stand alone. Is Heather's development normal, retarded, or advanced?

69. Clarke is 70 years old. She has always enjoyed food and has had a hearty appetite. Lately, however, she has complained that food "just doesn't taste as good anymore." What might be a possible explanation?

70. Mr. Ruiz, age 68, has noticed hearing problems, but only under certain circumstances. He has difficulty with certain tones, especially high or low tones, but has no problem with everyday conversation. What might be a possible explanation?

GROWTH/DEVELOPMENT

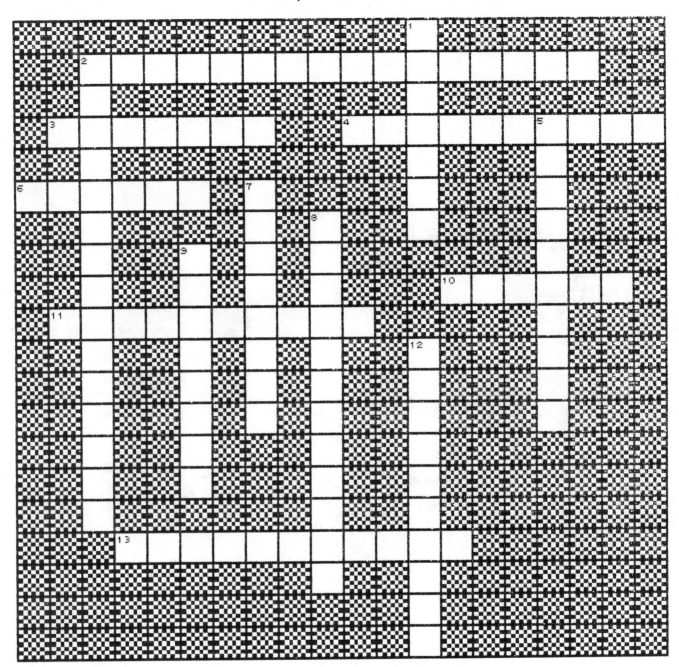

ACROSS

2. Hardening of the arteries
3. Will develop into a fetal membrane in the placenta
4. Old age
6. Name of zygote after 3 days
10. Fertilized ovum
11. Name of zygote after implantation
13. Process of birth

DOWN

1. First 4 weeks of infancy
2. Fatty deposit buildup on walls of arteries
5. Science of the development of the individual before birth
7. Eye disease marked by increased pressure in the eyeball
8. Study of how germ layers develop into tissues
9. Cloudy lens
12. Hardening of the lens

FERTILIZATION AND IMPLANTATION

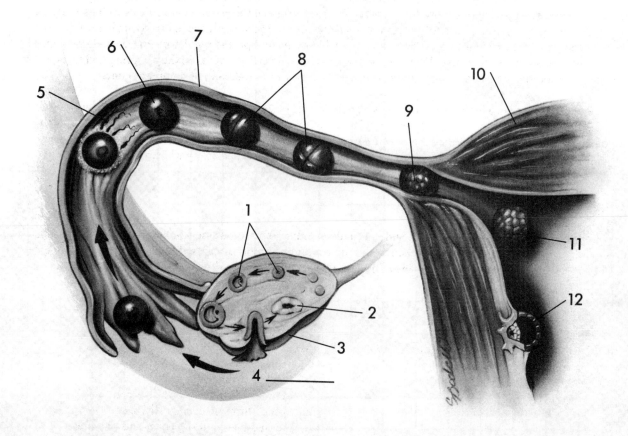

1. _____
2. _____
3. _____
4. _____
5. _____
6. _____

7. _____
8. _____
9. _____
10. _____
11. _____
12. _____

CHAPTER 23

Genetics and Genetic Diseases

Look about your classroom and you will notice various combinations of hair color, eye color, body size, skin tone, hair texture, sex, etc. Everyone has some unique body features and this phenomenon alerts us to the marvel of genetics. Independent units, called genes, are responsible for the inheritance of biological traits. Genes determine the structure and function of the human body by producing specific regulatory enzymes. Some genes are dominant and some are recessive. Dominant genes produce effects that appear in the offspring and recessive genes have effects that do not appear in the offspring when they are masked by a dominant gene.

Gene therapy is one of the latest advances of science. This revolutionary branch of medicine combines current technology with genetic research to unlock the secrets of the human body. Daily discoveries into the prevention, diagnosis, treatment, and cure of diseases and disorders are being revealed as a result of genetic therapy. A knowledge of genetics is necessary to understand the basic mechanism by which traits are transmitted from parents to offspring.

TOPICS FOR REVIEW

Your review of this chapter should include an understanding of chromosomes genes and gene expression. You should continue your study with a knowledge of common genetic diseases. Finally your review should conclude with an understanding of the prevention and treatment of genetic diseases.

GENETICS AND HUMAN DISEASE
CHROMOSOMES AND GENES

Match the term on the left with the proper selection on the right.

_____ 1. Gene
_____ 2. Chromosome
_____ 3. Gamete
_____ 4. Meiosis
_____ 5. Zygote

a. DNA molecule
b. Male or female reproductive cell
c. Special form of nuclear division
d. Formed by union of sperm and ovum at conception
e. Distinct code within a DNA molecule

► If you have had difficulty with this section, review pages 551-553. ◄

GENE EXPRESSION

Fill in the blanks.

After experimentation with pea plants, Mendel discovered that each inherited trait is controlled by two sets

of similar (6) _____, one from each parent. He also noted that some genes are (7)

_____ and some are (8) _____. In the example of albinism, a person with the gene combination of Aa is said to be a genetic (9) _____. If two different dominant genes occur together a form of dominance called (10) _____ exists.

(11) _____ chromosomes do not have matching structures. If an individual has the sex chromosomes XX, that person will have the sexual characteristics of a (12) _____.

(13) _____ simply means "change." A (14) _____ _____ is a change in the genetic code.

▸ If you have had difficulty with this section, review pages 553-556. ◂

GENETIC DISEASES

Choose the term that applies to each of the following descriptions. Place the letter for the term in the appropriate answer blank.

a. Single-gene disease
b. Nondisjunction
c. Monosomy
d. Fetal alcohol syndrome
e. Cystic fibrosis

f. Phenylketonuria
g. Down syndrome
h. Klinefelter's syndrome
i. Turner's syndrome
j. Cleft palate

_____ 15. Caused by recessive genes in chromosome pair 7.
_____ 16. Congenital disorder that is not inherited.
_____ 17. Congenital facial deformity that is inherited.
_____ 18. Results from a failure to produce the enzyme phenylalanine hydroxylase.
_____ 19. Presence of only one autosome instead of a pair.
_____ 20. Usually caused by trisomy of chromosome 21.
_____ 21. Cystic fibrosis is an example.
_____ 22. Results from nondisjunction of chromosomes and typically has the XXY pattern.
_____ 23. Term used to describe what happens when a pair of chromosomes fails to separate.
_____ 24. Sometimes called XO syndrome, it is treated with hormone therapy.

▸ If you have had difficulty with this section, review pages 557-560. ◂

PREVENTION AND TREATMENT OF GENETIC DISEASES

Circle the best answer.

25. A pedigree is a chart that can be used to determine:

a. Genetic relationships in a family over several generations
b. The possibility of producing offspring with certain genetic disorders
c. The possibility of a person developing a genetic disorder late in life
d. All of the above are correct
e. None of the above are correct

26. The Punnett Square is a grid used to determine:

    a. Genetic disorders
    b. The probability of inheriting genetic traits
    c. Proper gene replacement therapy
    d. The necessity for amniocentesis

27. Some forms of cancer are thought to be caused, at least in part, by abnormal genes called:

    a. Cancercytes
    b. Trisomy
    c. Oncogenes
    d. Autosomes

28. When producing a karyotype, the most common source of cells for the sample is the:

    a. Vagina
    b. Rectum
    c. Lining of the cheek
    d. Throat

29. An ultrasound transducer is used during amniocentesis to:

    a. Create a sharper image
    b. Take measurements during the procedure
    c. Prevent damaging rays during the procedure
    d. Guide the tip of the needle to prevent placental damage

30. Electrophoresis is a process that:

    a. Provides a method for DNA analysis
    b. Means electric separation
    c. Is the basis for DNA fingerprinting
    d. All of the above are correct

31. The use of genetic therapy began in 1990 with a group of young children having:

    a. AIDS
    b. Adenosine deaminase deficiency
    c. Hemophilia
    d. Cystic fibrosis

*If the statement is true, write **T** in the answer blank. If the statement is false, circle the incorrect word(s) and write the correct term in the answer blank.*

_____32. Chorionic villus sampling is a procedure in which cells that surround a young embryo are collected through the opening of the cervix.

_____33. Karyotyping is the process used for DNA fingerprinting.

_____34. In amniocentesis, normal genes are introduced with the hope that they will add to the production of the needed protein.

_____35. Deficiency of adenosine deaminase results in severe combined immune deficiency.

_____36. One hypothesis that may explain some forms of cancer is known as the tumor suppressor gene hypothesis.

► If you have had difficulty with this section, review pages 561-565. ◄

Unscramble the words.

37. RCRRIEA

38. YTSMOIR

39. EGNE

40. DPEREGIE

41. SOEMCROSHOM

Take the circled letters, unscramble them, and fill in the statement.

How Bill made his fortune.

ANSWER:

APPLYING WHAT YOU KNOW

43. John's mother has a dominant gene for dark skin color. John's father has a dominant gene for light skin color. What color will John's skin most likely be?

44. Mr. and Mrs. Freund both carry recessive genes for cystic fibrosis. Using your knowledge of the Punnett square, estimate the probability of one of their offspring inheriting this condition.

45. Linda is pregnant and is over 40. She fears her age may predispose her baby to genetic disorders and she has sought the advice of a genetic counselor. What tests might the counselor suggest to alleviate Linda's fears?

DID YOU KNOW?

Scientists now believe the human body has 50,000 to 100,000 genes packed into just 46 chromosomes.

PUNNETT SQUARE

Fill in the Punnett square for the following genetic cases:

Mr. Atkins has brown eyes (dominant) and Mrs. Atkins has blue eyes (recessive)

<u>Mr. Atkins PP</u>

	P	P
p		
p		

<u>Mrs. Atkins pp</u>

The offspring of Mr. and Mrs. Atkins have a _____ % chance of having brown eyes and a _____ % chance of having blue eyes.

Mr. and Mrs. Rhoades are both carriers for albinism. Using the Punnett square, determine what percentage of Mr. and Mrs. Rhoades' offspring will:

a. have normal pigmentation _____
b. be carriers _____
c. have albinism _____

<u>Mrs. Rhoades Pp</u>

	P	p
P		
p		

<u>Mr. Rhoades Pp</u>

ANSWERS TO EXERCISES

CHAPTER 1
AN INTRODUCTION TO THE STRUCTURE AND FUNCTION OF THE BODY

Matching

<u>Group A</u>

1. D, p. 2
2. E, p. 2
3. A, p. 2
4. C, p. 2
5. B, p. 2

<u>Group B</u>

6. C, p. 6
7. E, p. 6
8. A, p. 4
9. B, p. 6
10. D, p. 4

CROSSWORD

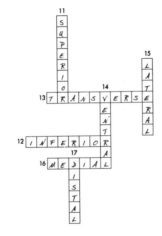

11. Superior
12. Inferior
13. Transverse
14. Ventral
15. Lateral
16. Medial
17. Distal

Did you notice that the answers were arranged as they appear on the human body?

Circle the correct answer

18. Inferior, p. 5
19. Anterior, p. 6
20. Lateral, p. 6
21. Proximal, p. 6
22. Superficial, p. 8
23. Equal, p. 9
24. Anterior and posterior, p. 9
25. Upper and lower, p. 9
26. Right upper quadrant, p. 8
27. Forward, p. 9

Circle the one that does not belong

28. Extremities (all others are part of the axial portions)
29. Cephalic (all others are part of the arm)
30. Plantar (all others are part of the face)
31. Eyes closed (all others are part of the anatomical position)
32. Plantar (all others are part of the trunk)
33. Carpal (all others are part of the leg or foot)
34. Thoracic (all others are located on the posterior sections of the body)

True or false

35. T
36. F (three stages), p. 12
37. T
38. F (they are not usually dissected), p. 12
39. F (during stage 3), p. 12
40. T

Fill in the blanks

41. Survival, p. 12
42. Internal environment, p. 12
43. Rise to toxic levels, p. 13
44. Developmental processes, p. 13
45. Aging processes, p. 13
46. Negative, positive, p. 13
47. Stabilizing, p. 13
48. Stimulatory, p. 13

APPLYING WHAT YOU KNOW

49.
50.
51.

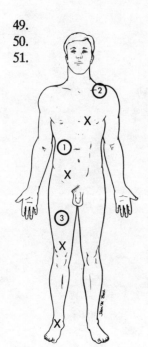

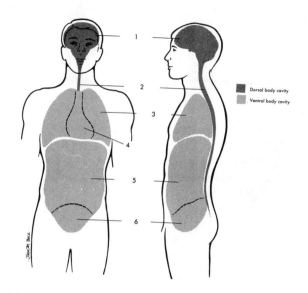

Dorsal and Ventral Body Cavities

1. Cranial cavity
2. Spinal cavity
3. Thoracic cavity

4. Mediastinum
5. Abdominal cavity
6. Pelvic cavity

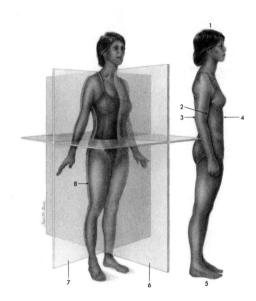

Directions and Planes of Body

1. Superior
2. Proximal
3. Posterior (Dorsal)
4. Anterior (Ventral)

5. Inferior
6. Sagittal plane
7. Frontal plane
8. Lateral

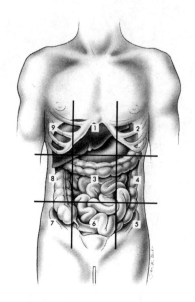

Regions of the Abdomen

1. Epigastric region
2. Left hypochondriac region
3. Umbilical region
4. Left lumbar region
5. Left iliac (inguinal) region

6. Hypogastric region
7. Right iliac (inguinal) region
8. Right lumbar region
9. Right hypochondriac region

CHAPTER 2
CELLS AND TISSUES

Matching

<u>Group A</u>

1. C, p. 20
2. E, p. 20
3. A, p. 20
4. B, p. 26
5. D, p. 25

<u>Group B</u>

6. D, p. 23
7. E, p. 24
8. A, p. 23
9. B, p. 23
10. C, p. 23

Fill in the blanks

11. Metric System, p. 21
12. Tissue typing, p. 24
13. Cilia, p. 25
14. Endoplasmic reticulum, p. 23
15. Ribosomes, p. 24
16. Mitochondria, p. 25
17. Lysosomes, p. 25
18. Golgi apparatus, p. 25
19. Centrioles, p. 25
20. Chromatin granules, p. 26
21. Rejection reaction, p. 24
22. ELISA, p. 24

Multiple choice

23. A, p. 26
24. D, p. 27
25. B, p. 27
26. D, p. 29
27. C, p. 29
28. A, p. 29
29. B, p. 28
30. C, p. 28
31. C, p. 29
32. A, p. 29
33. B, p. 28
34. A, p. 28

Circle the one that does not belong

35. Uracil (RNA contains the base uracil, not DNA)
36. RNA (the others are complementary base pairings of DNA)
37. Anaphase (the others refer to genes and heredity)
38. Thymine (the others refer to RNA)
39. Mitosis (the others refer to DNA before mitosis)
40. Prophase (the others refer to anaphase)
41. Prophase (the others refer to interphase)
42. Metaphase (the others refer to telophase)
43. Gene (the others refer to stages of cell division)

44. Fill in the missing area

TISSUE	LOCATION	FUNCTION
1.	1.	1a. Absorption by diffusion of respiratory gases between alveolar air and blood
		1b. Absorption by diffusion, filtration, and osmosis
2.	2a. Surface of lining of mouth and esophagus	2.
	2b. Surface of skin	
3.	3. Surface layer of lining of stomach, intestines, and parts of respiratory tract	3.
4. Stratified transitional	4.	4.
5.	5. Surface of lining of trachea	5.

1.	1. Between other tissues and organs	1.
2. Adipose	2.	2.
3.	3.	3. Flexible but strong connection
4.	4. Skeleton	4.
5.	5. Part of nasal septum, larynx, rings in trachea and bronchi, disks between vertebrae, external ear	5.
6.	6.	6. Transportation
7. Hemopoietic tissue	7.	7.

1.	1. Muscles that attach to bones, eyeball muscles, upper third of esophagus	1.
2. Cardiac	2.	2.

3.

3. Walls of digestive, respiratory, and genitourinary tracts; walls of blood and large lymphatic vessels; ducts of glands; intrinsic eye muscles; arrector muscles of hair

3.

1.

1. Brain and spinal cord, nerves

1.

APPLYING WHAT YOU KNOW

45.

46. Diffusion
47. Simple squamous epithelium
48. Merrily may have exceeded the 15% to 18% desirable body fat composition. Fitness depends more on the percentage and ratio of specific tissue types than the overall amount of tissue present.

CROSSWORD

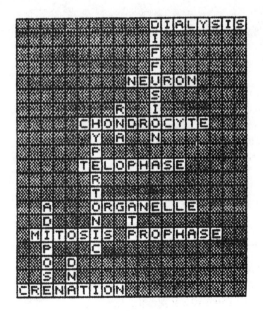

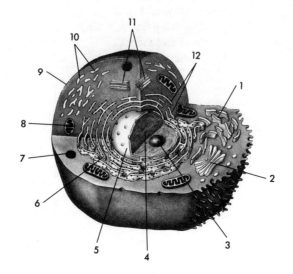

Cell Structure

1. Smooth endoplasmic reticulum
2. Golgi apparatus
3. Nucleolus
4. Nucleus
5. Nuclear membrane
6. Rough endoplasmic reticulum

7. Lysosome
8. Mitochondrion
9. Plasma membrane
10. Smooth endoplasmic reticulum
11. Centrioles
12. Ribosomes

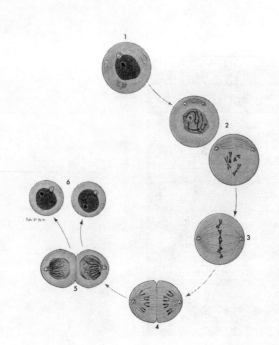

Mitosis

1. Interphase
2. Prophase
3. Metaphase

4. Anaphase
5. Telophase
6. Daughter cells (interphase)

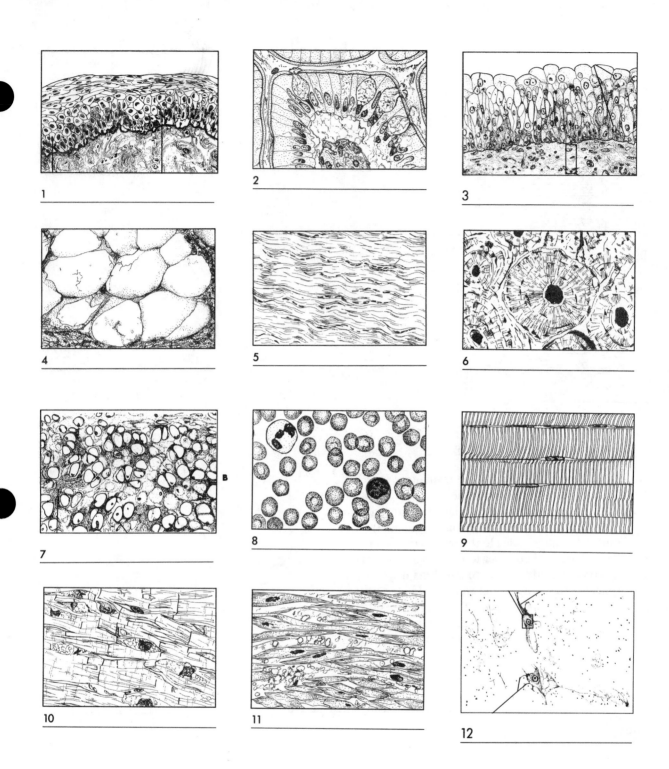

Tissues

1. Stratified squamous epithelium
2. Simple columnar epithelium
3. Stratified transitional epithelium
4. Adipose tissue
5. Dense fibrous connective tissue
6. Bone tissue
7. Cartilage
8. Blood
9. Skeletal muscle
10. Cardiac muscle
11. Smooth muscle
12. Nervous tissue

Matching

<u>Group A</u>

1. A, p. 57
2. E, p. 57
3. D, p. 57
4. B, p. 57
5. C, p. 57

<u>Group B</u>

6. F, p. 57
7. E, p. 57
8. B, p. 57
9. A, p. 57
10. C, p. 57
11. D, p. 57

Circle the one that does not belong

12. Mouth (the others refer to the respiratory system)
13. Rectum (the others refer to the reproductive system)
14. Pancreas (the others refer to the circulatory system)
15. Pineal (the others refer to the urinary system)
16. Joints (the others refer to the muscular system)
17. Pituitary (the others refer to the nervous system)
18. Tendons (the others refer to the skeletal system)
19. Appendix (the others refer to the endocrine system)
20. Thymus (the others refer to the integumentary system)
21. Trachea (the others refer to the digestive system)
22. Liver (the others refer to the lymphatic system)

Fill in the missing area

SYSTEM	ORGAN	FUNCTIONS
23.		Protection, regulation of body temperature, synthesis of chemicals and hormones, serves as a sense organ
24.	Bones, joints	
25.		Movement, maintains body

26. Nervous

posture, produces heat

27.

Pituitary, thymus, pineal,
adrenal, hypothalamus,
thyroid, pancreas, parathyroid,
ovaries, testes

28.

29.

Transportation, immunity

Lymph nodes, lymph vessels,
thymus, spleen, tonsils

30. Urinary

31.

Mouth, pharynx, esophagus,
stomach, small and large
intestine, rectum, anal canal,
teeth, salivary glands, tongue,
liver, gallbladder, pancreas,
appendix

32. Respiratory

a. Gonads - testes and
   ovaries

33.

b. Accessory glands (p. 57)
   Supporting structures (p.
   57)

Fill in the blanks

34. Nonvital organ, p. 66
35. Cochlear implants, p. 67
36. Dialysis machine, p. 67
37. Hemopump, p. 67
38. Organ transplantation, p. 67
39. Free-flap surgery, p. 69
40. Rejection, p. 69

Unscramble the words

41. Heart
42. Pineal
43. Nerve
44. Esophagus
45. Nervous

APPLYING WHAT YOU KNOW

46. (a) Endocrinology (endocrine system)
     (b) Gynecology (reproductive system)

47. The skin protects the underlying tissue against invasion by harmful bacteria. With a large percentage of Brian's skin destroyed, he was vulnerable to bacteria, and so he was placed in the cleanest environment possible - isolation. Jenny is required to wear special attire so that the risk of a visitor bringing bacteria to the patient is reduced.

CROSSWORD

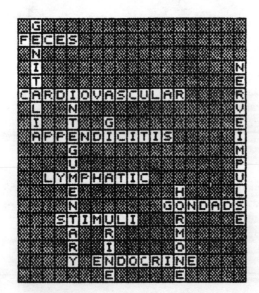

CHAPTER 4
MECHANISMS OF DISEASE

Matching

1. B, p. 74
2. E, p. 74
3. A, p. 74
4. C, p. 74
5. D, p. 74
6. C, p. 74
7. A, p. 74
8. D, p. 74
9. B, p. 74
10. E, p. 74

Fill in the blanks

11. Pathophysiology, p. 75
12. Homeostasis, p. 75
13. Mutated, p. 76
14. Parasite, p. 76
15. Neoplasms, p. 76
16. Self-immunity, p. 76
17. Risk factors, p. 77
18. Centers for Disease Control, p. 77
19. Psychogenic, p. 77
20. Secondary, p. 77

Multiple choice

21. C, p. 78
22. A, p. 78
23. B, p. 79
24. C, p. 80
25. D, p. 80
26. B, p. 81
27. D, p. 82
28. D, p. 82
29. B, p. 84
30. C, p. 85
31. E, p. 84
32. B, p. 87

Circle the correct response

33. Slowly, p. 87
34. Are not, p. 87
35. Papilloma, p. 88

36. Lymphoma, p. 89
37. Anaplasia, p. 89
38. Oncologist, p. 90
39. Biopsy, p. 90
40. Staging, p. 92
41. Appetite, p. 92

Seven Warning Signs of Cancer, p. 90

42. Sores that do not heal
43. Unusual bleeding
44. A change in wart or mole
45. A lump or thickening in any tissue
46. Persistent hoarseness or cough
47. Chronic indigestion
48. A change in bowel or bladder function

True or false

49. T, p. 92
50. F (slowly), p. 94
51. F (white), p. 94
52. T, p. 94
53. F (regeneration), p. 94
54. T, p. 95
55. T, p. 95

APPLYING WHAT YOU KNOW

56. No. Mrs. Calhoun most likely has a common cold.
57. Pinworm
58. Disinfection

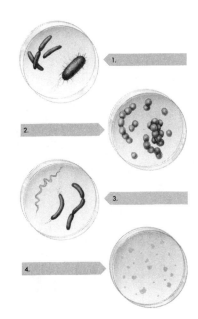

Major Groups of Pathogenic Bacteria

1. Bacilli (rods)
2. Cocci (spheres)
3. Curved rods
4. Small bacteria

Major Groups of Pathogenic Fungi

1. Yeasts
2. Molds

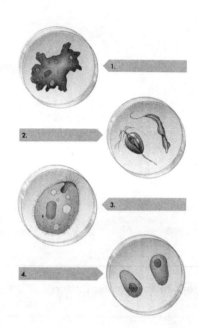

Major Groups of Pathogenic Protozoa

1. Amoebas
2. Flagellates
3. Ciliates
4. Sporozoa

Examples of Pathogenic Animals

1. Nematodes
2. Platyhelminths
3. Arthropods

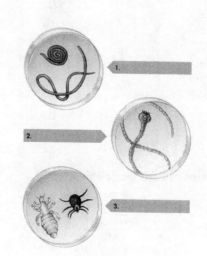

CHAPTER 5
THE INTEGUMENTARY SYSTEM AND BODY MEMBRANES

Select the best answer

1. B, p. 102
2. D, p. 104
3. C, p. 104
4. A, p. 102
5. B, p. 102
6. D, p. 104
7. C, p. 104
8. C, p. 104

Matching

Group A

9. D, p. 102
10. A, p. 104
11. B, p. 104
12. C, p. 112
13. E, p. 104

Group B

14. A, p. 105
15. D, p. 106
16. E, p. 106
17. C, p. 107
18. B, p. 106

Select the best answer

19. A, p. 105
20. B, p. 108
21. B, p. 107
22. A, p. 107
23. A, p. 105
24. B, p. 107
25. B, p. 108
26. B, p. 108
27. B, p. 108
28. A, p. 107

Fill in the blanks

29. Protection, temperature regulation, and sense organ activity, p. 111
30. Melanin, p. 112
31. Lanugo, p. 108
32. Hair papillae, p. 108
33. Alopecia, p. 108
34. Arrector pili, p. 109
35. Light touch, p. 109
36. Eccrine, p. 111
37. Apocrine, p. 111
38. Sebum, p. 111

Circle the correct answer

39. Will not, p. 113
40. Will, p. 113
41. Will not, p. 113
42. 11, p. 113
43. Third, p. 113

Choose the correct response

44. B, p. 112
45. A, p. 112
46. D, p. 114
47. D, p. 115
48. A, p. 117
49. D, p. 118
50. C, p. 118
51. A, p. 119

Unscramble the words

52. Epidermis
53. Keratin
54. Hair
55. Lanugo
56. Dehydration
57. Third Degree

APPLYING WHAT YOU KNOW

58. 46%
59. Pleurisy
60. Sunbathing. Mrs. Collins cannot repair UV damage and thus is very prone to skin cancer.

CROSSWORD

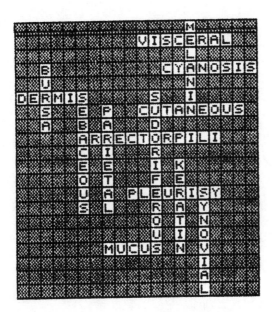

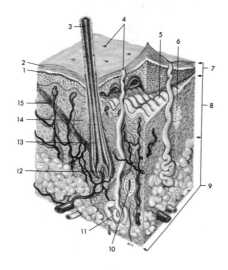

Longitudinal Section of the Skin

1. Pigment layer
2. Stratum corneum
3. Hair shaft
4. Openings of sweat ducts
5. Dermal papilla
6. Meissner's corpuscle
7. Epidermis
8. Dermis
9. Subcutaneous fatty tissue
10. Pacinian corpuscle
11. Sweat gland
12. Papilla of hair
13. Hair follicle
14. Sebaceous (oil) gland
15. Arrector pili muscle

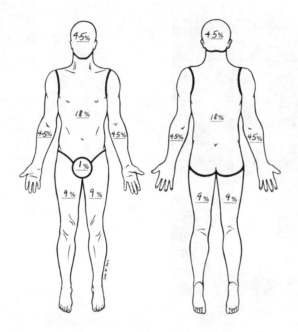

CHAPTER 6
THE SKELETAL SYSTEM

True or false

1. T
2. Epiphyses, not diaphyses, p. 128
3. Osteoblasts, not osteoclasts, p. 128
4. T
5. T
6. Juvenile, not adult, p. 129
7. Diaphysis, not articulation, p. 128
8. T
9. Ceases, not begins, p. 128
10. T

Matching

Group A

11. D, p. 130
12. B, p. 128
13. E, p. 130
14. A, p. 131
15. C, p. 131

16. D, p. 131
17. A, p. 131
18. E, p. 130
19. B, p. 131
20. C, p. 130

Fill in the blanks

21. 4, p. 132
22. Medullary cavity, p. 132
23. Articular cartilage, p. 133
24. Endosteum, p. 133
25. Hemopoiesis, p. 133

Multiple choice

26. A, p. 133
27. D, p. 136
28. A, p. 140
29. D, p. 142
30. C, p. 146
31. C, p. 149
32. D, p. 146
33. D, p. 146
34. A, p. 149
35. B, p. 136
36. A, p. 140
37. B, p. 146
38. B, p. 143
39. B, p. 147
40. C, p. 149
41. A, p. 149
42. D, p. 136
43. C, p. 138
44. C, p. 136

Circle the one that does not belong

45. Os coxae (all others refer to the spine)
46. Axial (all others refer to the appendicular skeleton)
47. Occipital (all others refer to a pair of sinuses)
48. Ribs (all others refer to the shoulder girdle)
49. Vomer (all others refer to the bones of the middle ear)
50. Ulna (all others refer to the os coxae bone)
51. Ethmoid (all others refer to the hand and wrist)
52. Nasal (all others refer to cranial bones)
53. Anvil (all others refer to the cervical vertebra)

Choose the right answer

54. A, p. 150
55. B, p. 150
56. B, p. 155
57. A, p. 150
58. B, p. 151

Matching

59. C, p. 136
60. G, p. 143
61. J, L, M, and K, p. 149
62. N, p. 149
63. I, p. 146
64. A, p. 136
65. P, p. 149
66. D, B, p. 136
67. F, p. 136
68. H, Q, p. 146
69. O, T, p. 149
70. R, p. 136
71. S, E, p. 136

Choose the better answer

72. Diarthroses, p. 151
73. Synarthrotic, p. 151
74. Diarthrotic, p. 153
75. Ligaments, p. 153
76. Articular cartilage, p. 153
77. Least movable, p. 154
78. Largest, p. 147
79. 2, p. 154
80. Mobility, p. 154
81. Pivot, p. 154

Fill in the blanks

82. Arthroscopy, p. 155
83. Osteosarcoma, p. 155
84. Osteomalacia, p. 156
85. Paget disease, p. 156
86. Osteomyelitis, p. 156
87. Simple fractures, p. 158
88. Comminuted fractures, p. 158
89. Osteoarthritis or degenerative joint disease (DJD), p. 159
90. Rheumatoid arthritis, gouty arthritis and infectious arthritis, p. 159
91. Lyme disease, p. 159

Unscramble the words

92. Vertebrae
93. Pubis
94. Scapula
95. Mandible
96. Phalanges
97. Pelvic girdle

APPLYING WHAT YOU KNOW

98. The bones are responsible for the majority of our blood cell formation. The disease condition of the bones might be inhibiting the production of blood cells for Mrs. Perine.

99. Epiphyseal cartilage is present only while a child is still growing. It becomes bone in adulthood. It is particularly vulnerable to fractures in childhood and preadolescence.

100. Osteoporosis

CROSSWORD

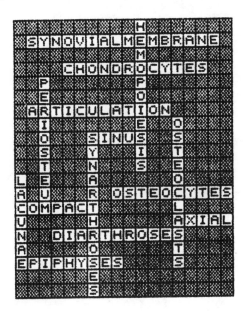

Long Bone

1. Articular cartilage
2. Spongy bone
3. Epiphyseal plate
4. Red marrow cavities
5. Compact bone
6. Medullary cavity
7. Yellow marrow
8. Periosteum

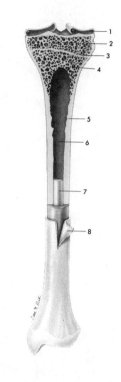

Anterior View of Skeleton

1. Orbit
2. Mandible
3. Sternum
4. Xiphoid process
5. Costal cartilage
6. Os coxae
7. Ilium
8. Pubis
9. Ischium
10. Frontal
11. Nasal
12. Maxilla
13. Clavicle
14. Ribs
15. Humerus
16. Vertebral column
17. Ulna
18. Radius
19. Sacrum
20. Coccyx
21. Carpals
22. Metacarpals
23. Phalanges
24. Femur
25. Patella
26. Tibia
27. Fibula
28. Tarsals
29. Metatarsals
30. Phalanges

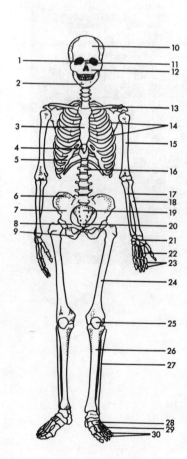

Posterior View of Skeleton

1. Parietal
2. Cervical vertebrae
3. Thoracic vertebrae
4. Lumbar vertebrae
5. Coccyx
6. Femur
7. Fibula
8. Tibia
9. Calcaneus
10. Occipital
11. Scapula
12. Ilium
13. Sacrum
14. Ischium

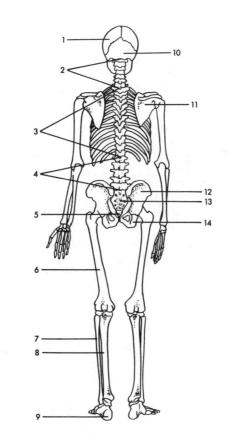

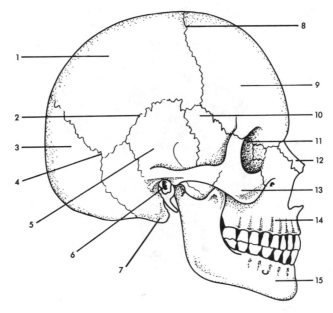

Skull - Right side

1. Parietal bone
2. Squamous suture
3. Occipital bone
4. Lambdoidal suture
5. Temporal bone
6. External auditory canal
7. Mastoid process
8. Coronal suture

9. Frontal bone
10. Sphenoid bone
11. Ethmoid bone
12. Nasal bone
13. Zygomatic bone
14. Maxilla
15. Mandible

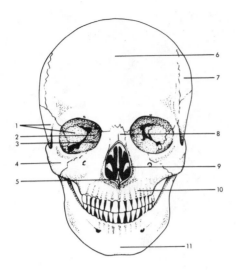

Skull - Front view

1. Sphenoid bone
2. Ethmoid bone
3. Lacrimal bone
4. Zygomatic bone
5. Vomer
6. Frontal bone

7. Parietal bone
8. Nasal bone
9. Inferior concha
10. Maxilla
11. Mandible

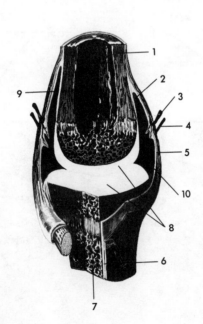

Structure of a Diarthrotic Joint

1. Bone
2. Synovial membrane
3. Blood vessel
4. Nerve
5. Joint capsule

6. Periosteum
7. Bone
8. Articular cartilage
9. Bursa

CHAPTER 7
THE MUSCULAR SYSTEM

Select the correct term

1. A, p. 166
2. B, p. 166
3. C, p. 166
4. C, p. 166
5. A, p. 166
6. B, p. 166
7. C, (may also be B), p. 166
8. A, p. 166
9. C, p. 166
10. C, p. 166

Matching

Groups A

11. D, p. 166
12. B, p. 166
13. A, p. 166
14. E, p. 166
15. C, p. 167

Group B

16. E, p. 167
17. C, p. 169
18. B, p. 169
19. A, p. 169
20. D, p. 169

Fill in the blanks

21. Pulling, p. 169
22. Insertion, p. 169
23. Insertion, origin, p. 169
24. Prime mover, p. 169
25. Antagonist, p. 169
26. Synergist, p. 169
27. Tonic contraction, p. 170
28. Muscle tone, p. 170
29. Hypothermia, p. 170
30. ATP, p. 170

True or false

31. Neuromuscular junction, p. 171
32. T
33. T
34. Oxygen debt, p. 170
35. "All or none", p. 172
36. Lactic acid, p. 170
37. Muscle tone, p. 174
38. T
39. Skeletal muscles, p. 171
40. T

Multiple choice

41. A, p. 172
42. B, p. 172
43. B, p. 172
44. C, p. 174
45. D, p. 173
46. A, p. 172
47. B, p. 172
48. C, p. 172
49. B, p. 173
50. D, p. 174

Matching

51. C, p. 175
52. F, p. 175; A and D, p. 183
53. F, p. 175 and B, p. 183
54. A, p. 175
55. C, p. 183
56. B, p. 183 and F, p. 175
57. A, p. 175
58. A and D, p. 175
59. B, p. 175
60. B, p. 175
61. A, p. 179 and E, p. 174
62. B, p. 174
63. D, p. 175

Multiple choice

64. A, p. 181
65. D, p. 182
66. C, p. 182
67. A, p. 182
68. D, p. 182
69. C, p. 182

Circle the correct response

70. Myalgia, p. 184
71. Myoglobin, p. 185
72. Poliomyelitis, p. 186
73. Myasthenia gravis, p. 186
74. Myasthenia gravis, p. 186

APPLYING WHAT YOU KNOW

75. Bursitis
76. Deltoid area
77. Tendon

78. WORD FIND

```
. . . . . . . N I G I R O I R . . . . . . .
. . . . . . . . . . S O N . . . . . N . .
. . . . M U S C L E O T O . R . . T O . .
. S . . . . . . . T C I . . O . . E I . .
. P . . . . . . O U X . . D T . . N X . .
. E . . . . N D E . . . E A . . O E . .
. C . . . . I B L . . . . T T . S S L . .
. I . . . C A F . . . . M A O B U Y F N
. B . . . . I . . . Y E G I R U I N . O
. . . . . . S . . S . H X A R . R Z O S I
. . . . . R . . . O . P T R T . S E V P T
. . . O . . . . . L . O E H S . A P I E R
. . D . . . . . . E . R N P . . . A T C E
. . . . . . . . . U . T S A . . . R I I S
. . . . . . . . . S . A I I . . . T S R N
. . . . . . . . . . O D . . . . . T I
. . T S I G R E N Y S N D I O T L E D . .
I S O M E T R I C . . . E U G I T A F .
. . . . . S U I M E N C O R T S A G . . .
. . S G N I R T S M A H . T E N D O N .
```

CROSSWORD

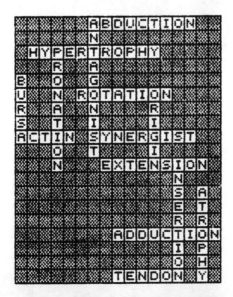

265

Muscles - Anterior View

1. Sternocleidomastoid
2. Trapezius
3. Pectoralis major
4. Rectus abdominis
5. External abdominal oblique
6. Iliopsoas
7. Quadriceps group
8. Tibialis anterior
9. Peroneus longus
10. Peroneus brevis
11. Soleus
12. Gastrocnemius
13. Sartorius
14. Adductor group
15. Brachialis
16. Biceps brachii
17. Deltoid
18. Facial muscles

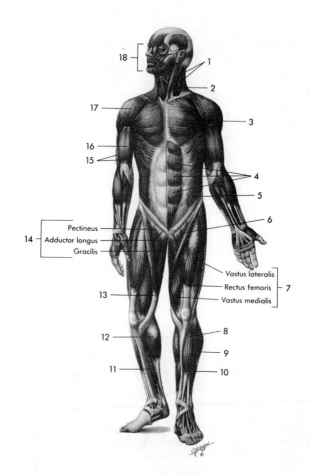

Muscles - Posterior View

1. Trapezius
2. External abdominal oblique
3. Gluteus maximus
4. Adductor magnus
5. Soleus
6. Peroneus brevis
7. Peroneus longus
8. Gastrocnemius
9. Hamstring group
10. Latissimus dorsi
11. Triceps brachii
12. Deltoid
13. Sternocleidomastoid

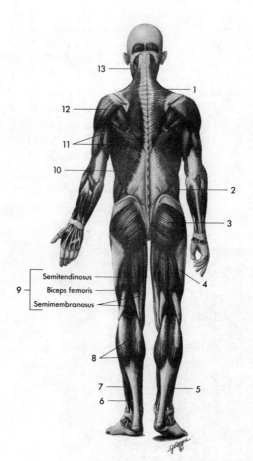

CHAPTER 8
THE NERVOUS SYSTEM

Matching

<u>Group A</u>

1. B, p. 194
2. C, p. 194
3. D, p. 194
4. A, p. 194

<u>Group B</u>

5. B, p. 194
6. D, p. 195
7. C, p. 194
8. A, p. 195
9. F, p. 198
10. E, p. 198

Select the best choice

11. A, p. 194
12. B, p. 194
13. B, p. 197
14. A, p. 194
15. A, p. 194
16. B, p. 197
17. B, p. 197
18. A, p. 194
19. B, p. 197
20. A, p. 195

Fill in the blanks

21. Two-neuron arc, p. 199
22. Sensory, interneurons, and motor neurons, p. 199
23. Receptors, p. 199
24. Synapse, p. 200
25. Reflex, p. 200
26. Withdrawal reflex, p. 200
27. Saltatory conduction, p. 203
28. Interneurons, p. 200
29. "Knee jerk", p. 200
30. Gray matter, p. 200

Circle the correct word

31. Do not, p. 201
32. Increases, p. 203
33. Excess, p. 203
34. Postsynaptic, p. 203
35. Presynaptic, p. 203
36. Neurotransmitter, p. 204
37. Communicate, p. 204
38. Specifically, p. 204
39. Sleep, p. 204
40. Pain, p. 204

Multiple choice

41. E, p. 210
42. D, p.
43. A, p.
44. E, p.
45. E, p.
46. D, p. 208
47. B, p. 208
48. E, p. 210
49. B, p. 209
50. D, p. 209
51. D, p. 208
52. B, p. 208
53. A, p. 210
54. D, p. 208
55. C, p. 208
56. H, p. 210
57. D, p. 210
58. E, p. 210
59. C, p. 211
60. J, p. 211
61. A, p. 211
62. B, p. 211
63. F, p. 211
64. I, p. 212
65. G, p. 212

True or false

66. 17 to 18 inches, p. 213
67. Bottom of the first lumbar vertebra, p. 213
68. Lumbar punctures, not CAT scan, p. 215
69. Spinal tracts, not dendrites, p. 213
70. T
71. One general function, not several, p. 213
72. Anesthesia, not paralysis, p. 216

Circle the one that does not belong

73. Ventricles (all others refer to meninges)
74. CSF (all others refer to the arachnoid)
75. Pia mater (all others refer to the cerebrospinal fluid)
76. Choroid plexus (all others refer to the dura mater)
77. Brain tumor (all others refer to a lumbar puncture)

CRANIAL NERVES

78.

NERVE	CONDUCT IMPULSES	FUNCTION
I Olfactory		
II		Vision
III	From brain to eye muscles	
IV Trochlear		
V		Sensations of face, scalp, and teeth, chewing movements
VI	From brain to external eye muscles	
VII		Sense of taste; contraction of muscles of facial expression
VIII Acoustic		
IX	From throat and taste buds of tongue to brain; also from brain to throat muscles and salivary glands	
X Vagus		
XI		Shoulder movements; turning movements of head
XII Hypoglossal		

Select the best choice

79. A, p. 219
80. B, p. 221
81. A, p. 220
82. B, p. 222
83. B, p. 220
84. A, p. 221
85. B, p. 220
86. B, p. 221

Matching

87. D, p. 225
88. E, p. 225
89. F, p. 225
90. B, p. 225
91. A, p. 225
92. C, p. 225

Multiple choice

93. C, p. 225
94. B, p. 225
95. B, p. 228
96. D, p. 225
97. A, p. 225
98. A, p. 228

Choose the correct response

99. B, p. 227
100. A, p. 227
101. A, p. 227
102. B, p. 227
103. A, p. 227
104. B, p. 227
105. A, p. 227
106. A, p. 227
107. B, p. 227
108. B, p. 227

Fill in the blanks

109. Acetylcholine, p. 228
110. Adrenergic fibers, p. 228
111. Cholinergic fibers, p. 228
112. Homeostasis, p. 228
113. Heart rate, p. 229
114. Decreased, p. 229

115. Neuroblastoma, p. 229

Unscramble the words

116. Neurons
117. Synapse
118. Autonomic
119. Smooth muscle
120. Sympathetic

APPLYING WHAT YOU KNOW

121. Right
122. Hydrocephalus
123. Sympathetic
124. Parasympathetic
125. Sympathetic; No, the digestive process is not active during sympathetic control. Bill may experience nausea, vomiting or discomfort because of this factor. See p. 227

CROSSWORD

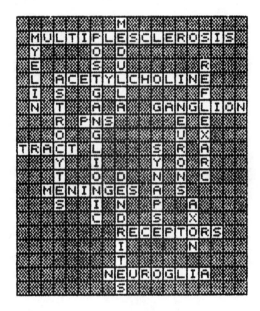

CROSSWORD

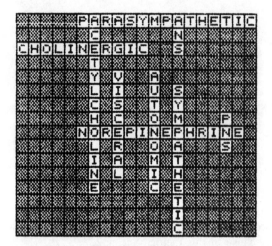

Neuron

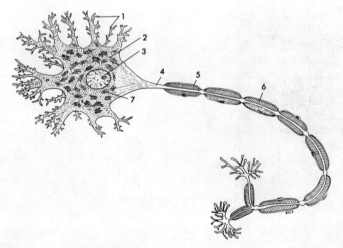

1. Dendrites
2. Cell body
3. Nucleus
4. Axon

5. Schwann cell
6. Myelin
7. Mitochondrion

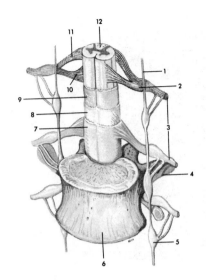

Spinal Cord

1. Sympathetic trunk
2. Spinal ganglion
3. Spinal nerves
4. Transverse process
5. Sympathetic ganglion
6. Body of vertebra

7. Dura mater
8. Arachnoid
9. Pia mater
10. Anterior root
11. Posterior root
12. Spinal cord

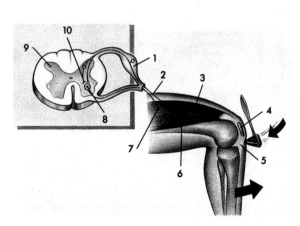

Patellar Reflex

1. Dorsal root ganglion
2. Sensory neuron
3. Stretch receptor
4. Patella
5. Patellar tendon

6. Quadriceps muscle
7. Motor neuron
8. Monosynaptic synapse
9. Gray matter
10. Interneuron

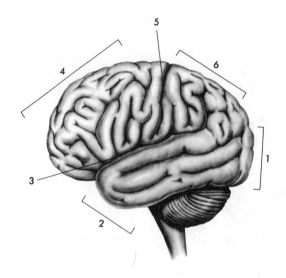

The Cerebrum

1. Occipital lobe
2. Temporal lobe
3. Fissure of Sylvius
4. Frontal lobe
5. Fissure of Rolando
6. Parietal lobe

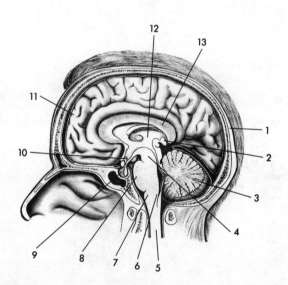

Sagittal Section of the Central Nervous System

1. Skull
2. Pineal gland
3. Cerebellum
4. Midbrain
5. Spinal cord
6. Medulla
7. Reticular formation
8. Pons
9. Pituitary gland
10. Hypothalamus
11. Cerebral cortex
12. Thalamus
13. Corpus callosum

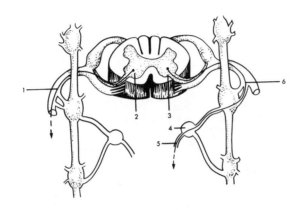

Neuron Pathways

1. Somatic motor neuron's axon
2. Cell body of somatic motor neuron
3. Cell body of preganglionic neuron
4. Collateral ganglion
5. Postganglionic neuron's axon
6. Preganglionic sympathetic neuron's axon

CHAPTER 9
SENSE ORGANS

Matching

1. D, p. 236
2. B, p. 252
3. A, p. 237
4. E, p. 252
5. C, p. 237

Multiple choice

6. C, p. 236
7. E, p. 236
8. B, p. 236
9. C, p. 236
10. E, p. 236
11. D, p. 236
12. A, p. 239
13. B, p. 239
14. C, p. 239
15. B, p. 239

16. D, p. 239
17. A, p. 237
18. D, p. 240

Select the best choice

19. C, p. 239
20. E, p. 241
21. F, p. 241
22. A, p. 241
23. J, p. 241
24. B, p. 242
25. H, p. 240
26. G, p. 243
27. I, p. 244
28. D, p. 242

Select the best choice

29. B, p. 245
30. C, p. 245
31. B, p. 245
32. A, p. 244
33. C, p. 246
34. A, p. 244
35. C, p. 246
36. B, p. 245
37. A, p. 244
38. C, p. 247

Fill in the blanks

39. Auricle and external auditory canal, p. 244
40. Eardrum, p. 244
41. Ossicles, p. 245
42. Oval window, p. 245
43. Otitis media, p. 245
44. Vestibule, p. 246
45. Mechanoreceptors, p. 246
46. Crista ampullaris, p. 247

Select the best choice

47. C, p. 247
48. A, p. 248
49. D, p. 248
50. E, p. 248
51. B, p. 248
52. F, p. 248

Circle the correct word

53. Papillae, p. 249
54. Cranial, p. 249
55. Mucus, p. 249
56. Memory, p. 250
57. Proprioception, p. 250

APPLYING WHAT YOU KNOW

58. External otitis
59. Cataracts
60. The eustachian tube connects the throat to the middle ear and provides a perfect pathway for the spread of infection
61. Hydrocephalus

62. **WORD FIND**

```
. . . . . . A V I T C N U J N O C . . .
. . . . . S U C N I . . . . . . . . . .
O L F A C T O R Y . . . . . . N . . . .
. . . . . . . . . . . . . P A . . . .
. C A T A R A C T S . . . H I . . . .
G U S T A T O R Y . . . O . . H . . . .
. . . P A P I L L A E T A R . C . . . .
. . . . . . . . . O I E . . A . . . .
. . C O C H L E A P P C . S . T . . . .
. C E R U M E N I O E . . E . S . . . .
. . . . . . . G Y P . . . N . U . . . .
. C O N E S M B T . . . . S . E . . . .
. . . . . . E S O A I P O R E P Y H . . .
. . . . N E R . . . . . . S . . . . . .
. . . . T R S . . . . . . . . . . . . .
. . . P M E C H A N O R E C E P T O R S
N O I T C A R F E R . . . . . E Y E . .
. . . . . . . . . . . . . . . . . . .
. . . . . . R O D S . . . . . . . . .
. . . . . . . . . . . . . . . . . . .
```

CROSSWORD

```
        V
TYMPANICMEMBRANE
        T
CRISTAEAMPULLARIS
R       R
E       O
T       U   SCLERA       C
I       H   E   Q   P     O
N       U   N   U   U     C
A       M   S   E   P     H
        O       OSSICLES
    CHOROID      U   L   E
        S           A
    ENDOLYMPH
                U
                M
                O
            AURICLE
```

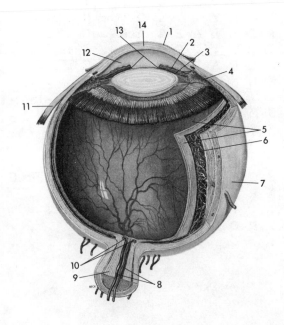

Eye

1. Conjunctiva
2. Iris
3. Posterior cavity
4. Ciliary muscle
5. Retina
6. Choroid layer
7. Sclera
8. Central retinal artery and vein
9. Optic nerve
10. Optic disc (blind spot)
11. Medial rectus muscle
12. Anterior cavity
13. Pupil
14. Cornea

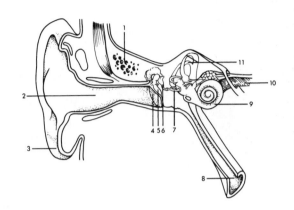

Ear

1. Temporal bone
2. External auditory canal
3. Auricle (Pinna)
4. Tympanic membrane (eardrum)
5. Malleus
6. Incus

7. Stapes
8. Auditory (Eustachian) tube
9. Cochlea
10. Cochlear nerve
11. Semicircular canals

CHAPTER 10
ENDOCRINE SYSTEM

Matching

<u>Group A</u>

1. D, p. 259
2. C, p. 259
3. E, p. 259
4. A, p. 259
5. B, p. 259

<u>Group B</u>

6. E, p. 263
7. C, p. 264
8. A, p. 258
9. D, p. 258
10. B, p. 258

Fill in the blanks

11. Second messenger, p. 258
12. Recognize, p. 258
13. First messengers, p. 258
14. Target organs, p. 258
15. Cyclic AMP, 258
16. Target cells, p. 258
17. Steroid abuse, p. 264

Multiple choice

18. B, p. 265
19. E, p. 265
20. D, p. 265
21. D, p. 265
22. A, p. 265
23. C, p. 267
24. C, p. 266
25. B, p. 265
26. A, p. 265
27. A, p. 265
28. D, p. 267
29. B, p. 267
30. A, p. 268
31. C, p. 268
32. C, p. 268

Select the best answer

33. A, p. 265
34. B, p. 265
35. B, p. 268
36. C, p. 268
37. A, p. 266
38. C, p. 268
39. A, p. 265
40. A, p. 265
41. A, p. 265
42. C, p. 268

Circle the correct term

43. Below, p. 268
44. Calcitonin, p. 268
45. Iodine, p. 268
46. Do not, p. 268
47. Thyroid, p. 268
48. Decrease, p. 268
49. Hypothyroidism, p. 271
50. Cretinism, p. 271

51. PTH, p. 271
52. Increase, p. 271

Fill in the blanks

53. Adrenal cortex and adrenal medulla, p. 272
54. Corticoids, p. 273
55. Mineralocorticoids, p. 273
56. Glucocorticoids, p. 273
57. Sex hormones, p. 274
58. Gluconeogenesis, p. 274
59. Blood pressure, p. 274
60. Epinephrine and norepinephrine, p. 274
61. Stress, p. 274
62. General adaptation syndrome, p. 276

Select the best response

63. A, p. 261
64. A, p. 274
65. B, p. 275
66. A, p. 276
67. B, p. 275
68. A, p. 273
69. A, p. 274

Circle the term that does not belong

70. Beta cells (all others refer to glucagon)
71. Glucagon (all others refer to insulin)
72. Thymosin (all others refer to female sex glands)
73. Chorion (all others refer to male sex glands)
74. Aldosterone (all others refer to the thymus gland)
75. ACTH (all others refer to the placenta)
76. Semen (all others refer to the pineal gland)

APPLYING WHAT YOU KNOW

77. She was pregnant
78. Zona reticularis of the adrenal cortex

79. WORD FIND

```
. . . . . H Y P E R C A L C E M I A . . . .
. . . . . . . A R . . . . E . . . . . . .
. . . . . . M . E . . D . N . . . . . . .
. . . . . E . . T . I . . O . . . . . . .
. . . . D . . . I . A . . M . . . . . . .
. . . E . N . . O . B . . R . . . . . . .
. . X . . . O . G . . E . O . . . . . . .
. Y . . . . . G . . T . H . . E . . . . .
M . . . . . . . A . . E . . . D N . . H .
. . . . . . . . . C . S . . I . D . . Y .
C R E T I N I S M . U . . U . . O . . P .
E X O C R I N E . . . L R . . . C . . O .
. . . . . . . . . . E G . . . R . G .
. . . . . . . . . . S . . . . I . L .
. . . . . . . . I . . . . . . N . Y .
. . . . . . . S . . . . . . . E . C .
. . S D I O C I T R O C . . . . . . E .
. S T R E S S S D I O R E T S . . . . M .
. . . . N O I T Z A I N I E T U L . . I .
. P R O S T A G L A N D I N S . . . . A .
```

CROSSWORD

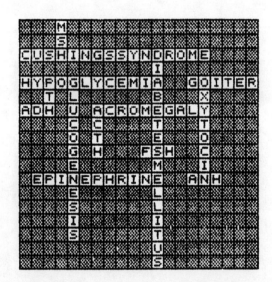

282

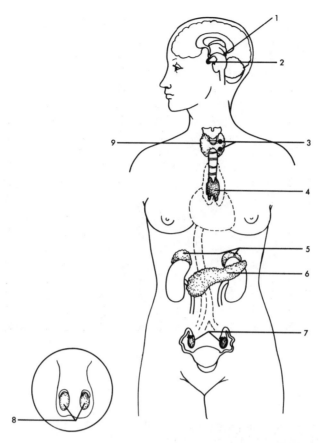

Endocrine Glands

1. Pineal
2. Pituitary
3. Parathyroids
4. Thymus
5. Adrenal

6. Pancreas
7. Ovaries
8. Testes
9. Thyroid

CHAPTER 11
BLOOD

Multiple choice

1. B, p. 288
2. C, p. 288
3. A, p. 291
4. B, p. 290
5. D, p. 288
6. C, p. 295
7. D, p. 291
8. A, p. 292
9. B, p. 292
10. B, p. 297
11. B, p. 288

12. E, p. 289
13. B, p. 288
14. C, p. 288
15. D, p. 288
16. E, p. 290
17. D, p. 290
18. B, p. 295
19. D, p. 289
20. B, p. 295
21. C, p. 295
22. B, p. 295
23. A, p. 297
24. E, p. 297
25. E, p. 297
26. D, p. 298
27. D, p. 298
28. B, p. 290
29. C, p. 292
30. A, p. 297
31. C, p. 298

Fill in the blank areas

32. p. 299

Blood Type	Antigen	Antibody
A	A	Anti-B
B	B	Anti-A
AB	A, B	None
O	None	Anti-A, Anti-B

Fill in the blanks

33. Antigen, p. 298
34. Antibody, p. 299
35. Agglutinate, p. 299
36. Erythroblastosis fetalis, p. 301
37. Rhesus monkeys, p. 301
38. Type O, p. 301
39. Type AB, p. 301

APPLYING WHAT YOU KNOW

40. No. If Mrs. Payne were a negative Rh factor and her husband were a positive Rh factor, it would set up the strong possibility of erythroblastosis fetalis.

41. Both procedures assist the clotting process.

284

42. WORD FIND

```
. . . S U B M O R H T . . . . . . . . . . .
. . R . B H E . P H A G O C Y T E S L .
. . E . A E M . . . . . . . . . . . E .
L . C . S M B . . . T H R O M B I N U .
E . I . O O O . . . . . . S . M . K .
U . P . P G L . . . . . E . O . . E .
K . I . H L U . A . . . T F N . . . M .
O . E . I O S . I . . Y A O . . . . I .
C S N . L B . . D . C C C . . . . A .
Y U T . . I . . S O T Y . . . . .
T S . R O N O D R O T . A . . . . .
E E . . . . H R E . N . . . . . .
S H N . . . T . . T A . . . . . .
. R I . . Y . . . I . N A M S A L P . .
. . R . R . . . G . T . E P Y T . . S
. . B E . . . E . . . I . . . . . E .
. . I . . . N . . . B . . . . R .
. . F . . A I M E N A O . . . . U . . .
N I R A P E H . . . . D . . . M . . . .
H E M A T O C R I T . Y . . . . . . . .
```

CROSSWORD

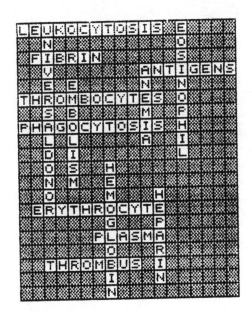

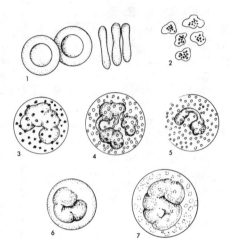

Human Blood Cells

1. Red blood cells
2. Platelets
3. Basophil
4. Neutrophil

5. Eosinophil
6. Lymphocyte
7. Monocyte

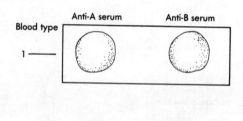

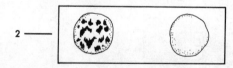

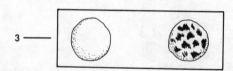

Normal blood

Agglutinated blood

Blood Types

1. O
2. A
3. B
4. AB

CHAPTER 12
THE HEART AND HEART DISEASE

Fill in the blanks

1. Circulatory system, p. 308
2. Interatrial septum, p. 308
3. Atria, p. 308
4. Ventricles, p. 308
5. Myocardium, p. 308
6. Endocarditis, p. 308
7. Bicuspid or mitral and tricuspid, p. 311
8. Visceral pericardium or epicardium, p. 311
9. Parietal pericardium, p. 311
10. Pericarditis, p. 311
11. Semilunar valves, p. 311
12. Mitral valve prolapse, p. 313
13. Rheumatic heart disease, p. 313

Select the best answer

14. F, p. 315
15. C, p. 316
16. D, p. 316
17. A, p. 313
18. B, p. 315
19. G, p. 316
20. E, p. 316
21. H, p. 316
22. J, p. 315
23. I, p. 316

Circle the correct response

24. B, p. 317
25. D, p. 317
26. A, p. 319
27. C, p. 320
28. A, p. 319
29. D, p. 319
30. C, p. 320
31. A, p. 321
32. B, p. 322
33. C, p. 321
34. A, p. 322
35. D, p. 321

APPLYING WHAT YOU KNOW

36. Coronary bypass surgery
37. Artificial pacemaker
38. The endocardial lining can become rough and abrasive to red blood cells passing over its surface. As a result, a fatal blood clot may be formed.

CROSSWORD

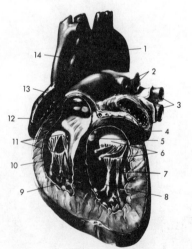

Heart

1. Aorta
2. Pulmonary arteries
3. Left pulmonary veins
4. Left atrium
5. Aortic semilunar valve
6. Bicuspid valve
7. Chordae tendineae

8. Left ventricle
9. Interventricular septum
10. Right ventricle
11. Tricuspid valve
12. Right atrium
13. Pulmonary semilunar valve
14. Superior vena cava

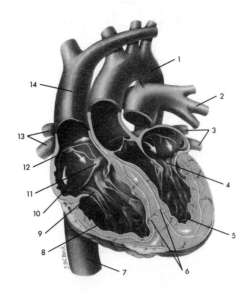

Conduction System of the Heart

1. Aorta
2. Pulmonary artery
3. Pulmonary veins
4. Mitral (bicuspid) valve
5. Left ventricle
6. Right and left branches of AV bundle
7. Inferior vena cava

8. Right ventricle
9. Tricuspid valve
10. Right atrium
11. Atrioventricular node (AV node)
12. Sinoatrial node (SA node or pacemaker)
13. Pulmonary veins
14. Superior vena cava

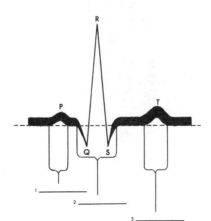

Normal ECG Deflections

1. Atrial depolarization
2. Ventricular depolarization
3. Ventricular repolarization

CHAPTER 13
CIRCULATION OF THE BLOOD

Matching

1. D, p. 328
2. B, p. 328
3. C, p. 328
4. G, p. 328
5. A, p. 328
6. E, p. 328
7. F, p. 328

Matching

8. I, p. 333
9. B, p. 333
10. D, p. 333
11. E, p. 333
12. A, p. 333
13. C, p. 334
14. F, p. 335
15. G, p. 335
16. J, p. 335
17. H, p. 335

Circle the correct choice

18. D, p. 336
19. C, p. 336
20. B, p. 336
21. B, p. 337
22. D, p. 339
23. B, p. 339
24. B, p. 339
25. A, p. 339
26. D, p. 332

True or false

27. Highest/arteries; lowest/veins, p. 339
28. Blood pressure gradient, p. 339
29. Stop, p. 340
30. High blood pressure, p. 340
31. Decreases, p. 340
32. T
33. T
34. T
35. Increases blood pressure/weaker heartbeat tends to decrease it, p. 341
36. Contract, p. 341

37. Relax, p. 341
38. T
39. T
40. Right, p. 343
41. Artery, p. 343
42. T
43. T
44. Brachial, p. 343

Fill in the blanks

45. Septic shock, p. 344
46. Cardiogenic shock, p. 344
47. Anaphylaxis, p. 344; Anaphylactic shock, p. 344
48. Neurogenic shock, p. 344
49. Low blood volume, p. 344
50. Toxic shock syndrome, p. 344

Unscramble the words

51. Systemic
52. Venule
53. Artery
54. Pulse
55. Vessel

APPLYING WHAT YOU KNOW

56. Anaphylactic shock
57. Hypovolemic shock
58. (a) Varicose veins
    (b) Wear support stockings

Fetal Circulation

1. Ductus arteriosus
2. Pulmonary artery
3. Pulmonary veins
4. Left atrium
5. Thoracic aorta
6. Left ventricle
7. Abdominal aorta
8. Hepatic artery
9. Kidney
10. Renal vein and artery
11. Intestine
12. Left common iliac artery
13. External iliac artery
14. Internal iliac arteries
15. Umbilical arteries
16. Placenta
17. Fetal umbilicus
18. Umbilical cord
19. Umbilical vein
20. Portal vein
21. Liver
22. Ductus venosus
23. Right ventricle
24. Inferior vena cava
25. Foramen ovale
26. Right atrium
27. Superior vena cava
28. Ascending aorta

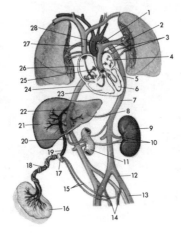

Hepatic Portal Circulation

1. Inferior vena cava
2. Stomach
3. Gastric vein
4. Left gastroepiploic vein
5. Spleen
6. Splenic vein with pancreatic branches
7. Tail of pancreas
8. Right gastroepiploic vein
9. Descending colon
10. Inferior mesenteric vein
11. Small intestine
12. Appendix
13. Superior mesenteric vein
14. Ascending colon
15. Head of pancreas
16. Duodenum
17. Hepatic portal vein
18. Cystic vein
19. Liver
20. Hepatic veins

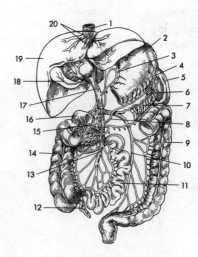

292

Principal Arteries of the Body

1. Occipital
2. Internal carotid
3. External carotid
4. Left common carotid
5. Left subclavian
6. Arch of aorta
7. Pulmonary
8. Left coronary
9. Aorta
10. Celiac
11. Splenic
12. Renal
13. Inferior mesenteric
14. Radial
15. Ulnar
16. Anterior tibial
17. Popliteal
18. Femoral
19. Deep femoral
20. External iliac
21. Internal iliac
22. Common iliac
23. Abdominal aorta
24. Superior mesenteric
25. Brachial
26. Axillary
27. Right coronary
28. Brachiocephalic
29. Right common carotid
30. Facial

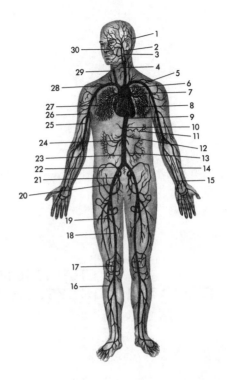

Principal Veins of the Body

1. Superior sagittal sinus
2. External jugular
3. Internal jugular
4. Left brachiocephalic
5. Left subclavian
6. Cephalic
7. Axillary
8. Left coronary
9. Basilic
10. Long thoracic
11. Splenic
12. Inferior mesenteric
13. Common iliac
14. Internal iliac
15. Femoral
16. Popliteal
17. Peroneal
18. Posterior tibial

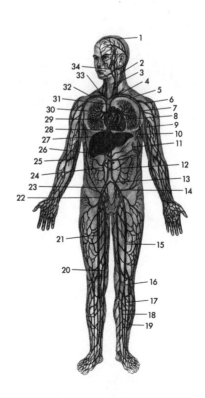

19. Anterior tibial
20. Great saphenous
21. Femoral
22. External iliac
23. Common iliac
24. Superior mesenteric
25. Median cubital
26. Portal
27. Hepatic
28. Inferior vena cava
29. Right coronary
30. Pulmonary
31. Superior vena cava
32. Right subclavian
33. Right brachiocephalic
34. Anterior facial

CHAPTER 14
THE LYMPHATIC SYSTEM AND IMMUNITY

Fill in the blanks

1. Lymph, p. 350
2. Interstitial fluid, p. 350
3. Lymphatic capillaries, p. 350
4. Right lymphatic duct and thoracic duct, p. 350
5. Cisterna chyli, p. 350
6. Lymph nodes, p. 352
7. Afferent, p. 352
8. Efferent, p. 352
9. Lymphedema, p. 351
10. Lymphoma, p. 353

Choose the correct response

11. B, p. 354
12. C, p. 354
13. C, p. 354
14. A, p. 353
15. C, p. 354
16. A, p. 353
17. A, p. 353

Matching

18. C, p. 355
19. A, p. 355
20. E, p. 355
21. B, p. 355
22. D, p. 355

Matching

23. C, p. 357
24. A, p. 356
25. F, p. 357
26. B, p. 357
27. G, p. 356
28. D, p. 358
29. H, p. 359
30. E, p. 358

Circle the best answer

31. D, p. 360
32. D, p. 361
33. C, p. 361
34. C, p. 360
35. C, p. 360
36. E, p. 360
37. E, p. 360
38. C, p. 360
39. E, p. 360
40. E, p. 362
41. A, p. 360
42. B, p. 362

Circle the correct response

43. Hypersensitivity, p. 363
44. Allergens, p. 364
45. Anaphylactic shock, p. 364
46. Lupus, p. 365
47. Isoimmunity, p. 365
48. HLAs, p. 365

Select the correct response

49. B, p. 366
50. A, p. 366
51. A, p. 366
52. B, p. 366
53. A, p. 366

Unscramble the words

54. Complement
55. Immunity
56. Clones
57. Interferon
58. Memory cells

APPLYING WHAT YOU KNOW

59. Natural active immunity
60. AIDS
61. Baby Coyle had no means of producing T cells, thus making him susceptible to several diseases. Isolation was a means of controlling his exposure to these diseases.

CROSSWORD

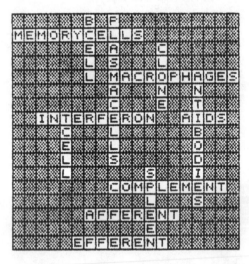

B Cell Development

1. Immature B cells
2. Activated B cells
3. Memory cells
4. Antibodies

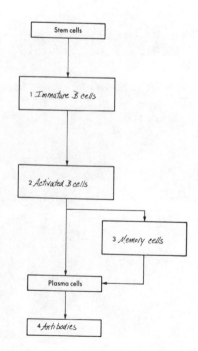

Function of Sensitized T Cells

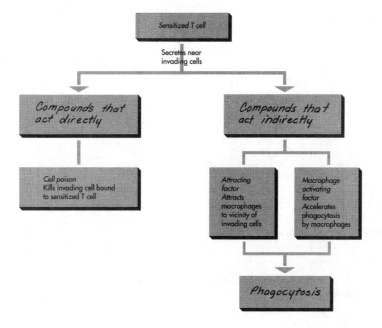

Function of Antibodies

1. Antigen
2. Antibody
3. Antigen
4. Antibody complex
5. Kills invader

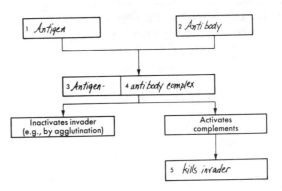

CHAPTER 15
THE RESPIRATORY SYSTEM

Matching

1. J, p. 376
2. G, p. 378
3. A, p. 376
4. I, p. 379
5. B, p. 379
6. F, p. 379
7. C, p. 376
8. H, p. 378
9. D, p. 376
10. E, p. 376

Fill in the blanks

11. Air distributor, p. 376
12. Gas exchanger, p. 376
13. Filters, p. 376
14. Warms, p. 376
15. Humidifies, p. 376
16. Nose, p. 376
17. Pharynx, p. 376
18. Larynx, p. 376
19. Trachea, p. 376
20. Bronchi, p. 376
21. Lungs, p. 376
22. Alveoli, p. 376
23. Diffusion, p. 376
24. Respiratory membrane, p. 376
25. Surface, p. 376

Circle the one that does not belong

26. Oropharynx (the others refer to the nose)
27. Conchae (the others refer to paranasal sinuses)
28. Epiglottis (the others refer to the pharynx)
29. Uvula (the others refer to the adenoids)
30. Larynx (the others refer to the eustachian tubes)
31. Tonsils (the others refer to the larynx)
32. Eustachian tube (the others refer to the tonsils)
33. Pharynx (the others refer to the larynx)

Choose the correct response

34. A, p. 380
35. B, p. 381
36. A, p. 379
37. A, p. 380
38. A, p. 379
39. B, p. 382
40. B, p. 381
41. C, p. 383
42. C, p. 383
43. B, p. 383
44. A, p. 383

Fill in the blanks

45. Trachea, p. 383
46. C-rings of cartilage, p. 384
47. Heimlich maneuver, p. 385
48. Primary bronchi, p. 385
49. Alveolar sacs, p. 385
50. Apex, p. 387

51. Pleura, p. 387
52. Pleurisy, p. 387
53. Pneumothorax, p. 388

True or false

54. Breathing, p. 389
55. Expiration, p. 390
56. Down, p. 390
57. Internal respiration, p. 389
58. T
59. 1 pint, p. 393
60. T
61. Vital capacity, p. 393
62. T

Multiple choice

63. E, p. 389
64. C, p. 392
65. C, p. 391
66. B, p. 390
67. D, p. 393
68. D, p. 393
69. D, p. 393

Matching

70. E, p. 394
71. B, p. 396
72. G, p. 396
73. A, p. 396
74. F, p. 396
75. D, p. 396
76. C, p. 396

Fill in the blanks

77. Pneumonia, p. 398
78. Tuberculosis, p. 398
79. Emphysema, p. 399
80. Asthma, p. 399

Unscramble the words

81. Pleurisy
82. Bronchitis
83. Epistaxis
84. Adenoids

85. Inspiration

APPLYING WHAT YOU KNOW

86. During the day Peter's cilia are paralyzed because of his heavy smoking. They use the time, when Peter is asleep, to sweep accumulations of mucus and bacteria towards the pharynx. When Peter awakes, these collections are waiting to be eliminated.

87. Swelling of the tonsils or adenoids caused by infection may make it difficult or impossible for air to travel from the nose into the throat. The individual may be forced to breathe through the mouth.

CROSSWORD

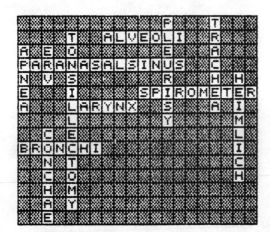

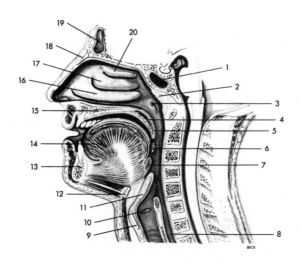

Sagittal View of Face and Neck

1. Sphenoid air sinus
2. Pharyngeal tonsil (adenoids)
3. Auditory tube
4. Soft palate
5. Uvula
6. Palatine tonsil
7. Lingual tonsil
8. Esophagus
9. Thyroid cartilage
10. Vocal cords

11. Epiglottis
12. Hyoid bone
13. Mandible
14. Tongue
15. Hard palate
16. Inferior concha
17. Middle concha
18. Nasal bone
19. Frontal air sinus
20. Superior concha

Respiratory Organs

1. Pharynx
2. Left main bronchus
3. Bronchioles
4. Right main bronchus
5. Trachea
6. Alveolar sacs
7. Alveolar duct
8. Alveolus
9. Capillary

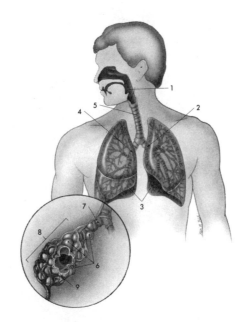

Pulmonary Ventilation Volumes

1. Total lung capacity
2. Inspiratory reserve volume
3. Tidal volume
4. Expiratory reserve volume
5. Residual volume

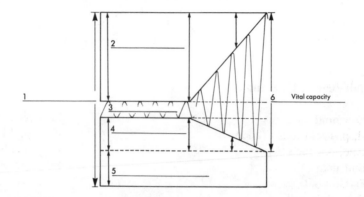

CHAPTER 16
THE DIGESTIVE SYSTEM

Fill in the blanks

1. Gastrointestinal tract or G.I. tract, p. 404
2. Mechanical, p. 404
3. Chemical, p. 404
4. Feces, p. 404
5. Digestion, absorption, and metabolism, p. 404
6. Parietal peritoneum, p. 404
7. Mouth, anus, p. 404
8. Lumen, p. 404
9. Mucosa, p. 404
10. Submucosa, p. 404
11. Peristalsis, p. 404
12. Serosa, p. 404
13. Mesentery, p. 404

Choose the correct answer

14. A, p. 405
15. B, p. 405
16. B, p. 405
17. A, p. 405
18. A, p. 405
19. A, p. 405
20. A, p. 405
21. A, p. 405
22. B, p. 405
23. B, p. 405
24. B, p. 405
25. B, p. 405

Multiple choice

26. E, p. 406
27. C, p. 407
28. E, p. 408
29. D, p. 409
30. B, p. 409
31. C, p. 408
32. D, p. 408
33. D, p. 408
34. D, p. 410
35. B, p. 411
36. C, p. 410
37. A, p. 410
38. A, P. 408
39. B, p. 408
40. C, p. 408

Fill in the blanks

41. Pharynx, p. 411
42. Esophagus, p. 411
43. Stomach, p. 411
44. Cardiac sphincter, p. 412
45. Chyme, p. 413
46. Fundus, p. 413
47. Body, p. 413
48. Pylorus, p. 413
49. Pyloric sphincter, p. 413
50. Small intestine, p. 413

Matching

51. D, p. 413
52. J, p. 413
53. G, p. 413

54. A, p. 411
55. H, p. 414
56. B, p. 413
57. C, p. 413
58. E, p. 413
59. I, p. 412
60. F, p. 413

Multiple choice

61. C, p. 415
62. B, p. 415
63. A, p. 417
64. A, p. 418
65. B, p. 415
66. E, p. 415
67. D, p. 418
68. D, p. 417
69. B, p. 417
70. C, p. 417

True or false

71. Vitamin K, p. 420
72. No villi are present in the large intestine, p. 420
73. Diarrhea, p. 421
74. Cecum, p. 420
75. Hepatic, p. 420
76. Sigmoid, p. 421
77. T
78. T
79. Parietal, p. 424
80. Mesentery, p. 424
81. Diverticulitis, p. 422
82. T
83. T
84. Ascites, p. 425

Multiple choice

85. B, p. 427
86. D, p. 426
87. C, p. 427
88. C, p. 426
89. C, p. 426

90. Fill in the blank areas on the chart below.

CHEMICAL DIGESTION

DIGESTIVE JUICES AND ENZYMES	SUBSTANCE DIGESTED (OR HYDROLYZED)	RESULTING PRODUCT
SALIVA		
	1. Starch (polysaccharide)	
GASTRIC JUICE		
		2. Partially digested proteins
PANCREATIC JUICE		
		3. Starch, peptides and amino acids
	4. Fats emulsified by bile	
INTESTINAL JUICE		
	5. Peptides	
6. Sucrase		
	7. Lactose	
		8. Glucose

APPLYING WHAT YOU KNOW

91. Ulcer
92. Pylorospasm
93. Basal metabolic rate or protein-bound iodine to determine thyroid function

94. WORD FIND

```
. . . . . . . . . N . . . . . . . . . . U . E
. . . . . . . N X O . . . . . . . . . V . C
. . . . . . N . R I I . . . . . . . U . I
. S . P F . O . . U D T . . . . . L . D
. A . A E . I . . . B N A . . . . A . N
. E . P C . T D . . . T E C . . . . U
D R . I E . S E . . . . R P I . . . . A
I C . L S . E N . . . . . A P T . . . J
A N C L . . G T . . . . . F E A S . . P
R A A A . . I I . . . . U . . H . A . E
R P V E N . D N . . . N . . . E . . M R
H . I . . W . D . D . . . . . M . . M I
E . T . . . O U . U . A S O C U M . E S
A . Y . . . O R S . . . . . . L . . S T
. . . . . D . . C . . . . . . S . . E A
. . . N E N O I T P R O S B A I . . N L
. . . N . S T O M A C H . . . F . . T S
. . U . . . . . . . . . . . . Y . . E I
. M . . . . . . . . . . . . . . . . R S
. M E T A B O L I S M . . . . . . . . Y .
```

CROSSWORD

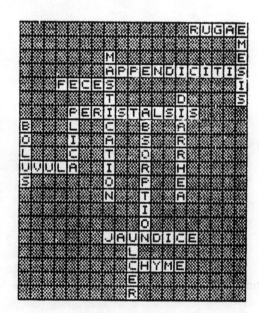

306

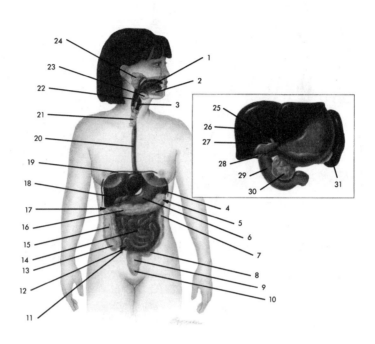

Digestive Organs

1. Tongue
2. Sublingual gland
3. Larynx
4. Spleen
5. Splenicflexure
6. Stomach
7. Descending colon
8. Sigmoid colon
9. Rectum
10. Anal canal

11. Veriform appendix
12. Region of ileocecal valve
13. Cecum
14. Ileum
15. Ascending colon
16. Transverse colon
17. Hepatic flexure
18. Liver
19. Diaphragm
20. Esophagus

21. Trachea
22. Pharynx
23. Submandibular gland
24. Parotid gland
25. Hepatic bile duct
26. Liver
27. Cystic duct
28. Gallbladder
29. Duodenum
30. Pancreas
31. Spleen

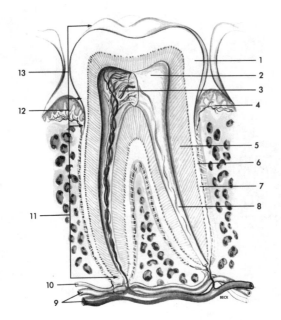

Tooth

1. Enamel
2. Pulp
3. Pulp cavity
4. Gingiva (gum)
5. Dentin
6. Periodontal membrane
7. Cementum
8. Root canal
9. Vein and artery
10. Nerve
11. Root
13. Neck
14. Crown

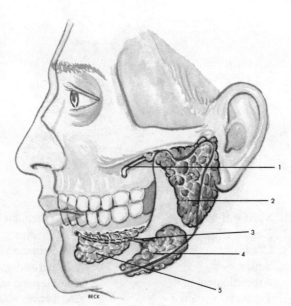

The Salivary Glands

1. Parotid duct
2. Parotid gland
3. Submandibular duct
4. Submandibular gland
5. Sublingual gland

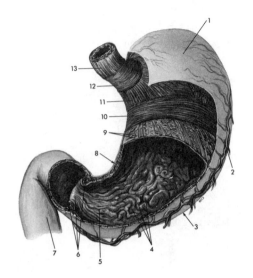

Stomach

1. Fundus
2. Body
3. Greater curvature
4. Rugae
5. Pylorus
6. Pyloric sphincter
7. Duodenum

8. Lesser curvature
9. Oblique muscle layer
10. Circular muscle layer
11. Longitudinal muscle
12. Cardiac sphincter
13. Esophagus

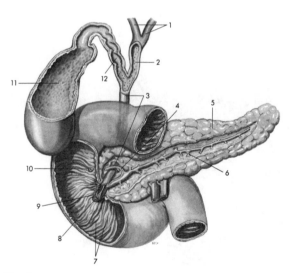

Gallbladder and Bile Ducts

1. Right and left hepatic ducts
2. Common hepatic duct
3. Common bile duct
4. Accessory duct
5. Pancreas
6. Pancreatic duct

7. Duodenum
8. Major duodenal papilla
9. Sphincter muscles
10. Minor duodenal papilla
11. Gallbladder
12. Cystic duct

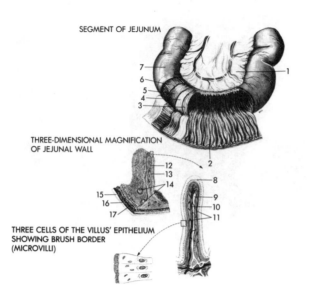

SEGMENT OF JEJUNUM

THREE-DIMENSIONAL MAGNIFICATION
OF JEJUNAL WALL

THREE CELLS OF THE VILLUS' EPITHELIUM
SHOWING BRUSH BORDER
(MICROVILLI)

The Small Intestine

1. Mesentery
2. Plica
3. Mucosa
4. Submucosa
5. Circular muscle
6. Longitudinal muscle
7. Serosa
8. Epithelium of villus
9. Lacteal

10. Artery
11. Vein
12. Plica
13. Submucosa
14. Lymph nodules
15. Serosa
16. Circular muscle
17. Longitudinal muscle

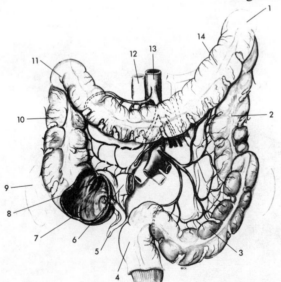

The Large Intestine

1. Splenic flexure
2. Descending colon
3. Sigmoid colon
4. Rectum
5. Vermiform appendix
6. Ileum
7. Cecum

8. Ileocecal valve
9. Ilium
10. Ascending colon
11. Hepatic flexure
12. Inferior vena cava
13. Aorta
14. Transverse colon

310

CHAPTER 17
NUTRITION AND METABOLISM

Fill in the blanks

1. Bile, p. 434
2. Prothrombin, p. 434
3. Fibrinogen, p. 434
4. Iron, p. 434
5. Hepatic portal vein, p. 434

Matching

6. B, p. 437
7. A, p. 434
8. C, p. 437
9. D, p. 438
10. E, p. 439
11. A, p. 434
12. E, p. 439
13. A, p. 434

Circle the word that does not belong

14. Bile (all others refer to Carbohydrate Metabolism)
15. Amino acids (all others refer to Fat Metabolism)
16. M (all others refer to Vitamins)
17. Pyruvic acid (all others refer to Protein Metabolism)
18. Insulin (all others tend to increase blood glucose)
19. Folic acid (all others are Minerals)
20. Ascorbic acid (all others refer to the B-complex vitamins)

Choose the correct response

21. B, p. 442
22. C, p. 442
23. G, p. 443
24. F, p. 442
25. A, p. 442
26. H, p. 443
27. E, p. 442
28. D, p. 442
29. C, p.
30. A, p.
31. C, p. 444
32. B, p. 444
33. B, p. 445
34. A, p. 444
35. C, p. 445

36. D, p. 445
37. A, p. 442

True or false

38. T
39. Hypothermia, p. 446
40. T
41. Heat stroke, p. 446
42. Malignant hyperthermia, p. 446

Unscramble the words

43. Liver
44. Catabolism
45. Amino
46. Pyruvic
47. Evaporation

APPLYING WHAT YOU KNOW

48. Weight loss and Anorexia nervosa
49. (a) Iron
    (b) Meat, eggs, vegetables and legumes

50. WORD FIND

```
M I N E R A L S . . . . . . . . . . . .
. . . . C . . . . . . C O N V E C T I O N
. . . . . A . . I B P . . . R M T . . .
. P . . . R . . . . . . . . . . . C .
. T . . . . B . R A D I A T I O N A .
. A . . . . . O . . . . . . . . T A .
. . . . . . . H . . . . . . . . A B .
. . . . . . . Y . . . . . . . . B O .
N . F . . . . . . D . . . . . O L .
O . . A . . . . . L O R E C Y L G L .
I . . . T . . B M R . . A . . . . I .
T . . . . S . . . R E V I L T . . . S .
C . . . . . . . . . . . . . E . . M .
U . . . . . . . . . . . . . . S . . .
D S N I E T O R P . . . . . . . . . .
N . . . . . . . A D I P O S E . . . .
O . . . . . . . N O I T A R O P A V E .
C . . . . . . . . E L I B . . . . . .
. . . . . . S I S Y L O C Y L G . . . .
. . . . . . . . V I T A M I N S . . . .
```

312

CROSSWORD

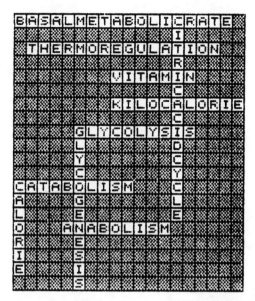

**CHAPTER 18
URINARY SYSTEM**

Multiple choice

1. E, p. 452
2. C, p. 452
3. E, p. 452
4. C, p. 457
5. E, p. 459
6. C, p. 457
7. B, p. 459
8. E, p. 459
9. C, p. 459
10. C, p. 459
11. B, p. 460 (review Chapter 10)
12. D, p. 460

Choose the correct term

13. G, p. 452
14. I, p. 454
15. H, p. 452
16. B, p. 452
17. K, p. 457
18. F, p. 452
19. J, p. 452
20. D, p. 452
21. L, p. 457
22. C, p. 452

23. E, p. 452
24. A, p. 452

Choose the correct term

25. C, p. 452
26. B, p. 462
27. C, p. 463
28. A, p. 461
29. B, p. 462
30. C, p. 463
31. C, p. 463
32. A, p. 461
33. C, p. 462
34. B, p. 462
35. A, p. 461
36. B, p. 463

Fill in the blanks

37. Urinalysis, p. 461
38. Mucous membrane, p. 463
39. Centrifuge, p. 461
40. Anuria, p. 460
41. Bladder infections or Cystitis, p. 454
42. Semen, p. 463
43. Urinary meatus, p. 463

Fill in the blanks

44. Micturition, p. 463
45. Urination, p. 463
46. Voiding, p. 463
47. Internal urethral sphincter, p. 463
48. Exit, p. 463
49. Urethra, p. 463
50. Voluntary, p. 463
51. Emptying reflex, p. 463
52. Urethra, p. 463
53. Retention, p. 463
54. Suppression, p. 463
55. Automatic bladder, p. 463

Select the best choice

56. I, p. 464
57. C, p. 464
58. G, p. 464
59. F, p. 464
60. K, p. 464

61. A, p. 465
62. H, p. 467
63. J, p. 467
64. B, p. 464
65. D, p. 465
66. E, p. 465
67. L, p. 464

APPLYING WHAT YOU KNOW

68. Polyuria
69. Residual urine is often the cause of repeated cystitis

70. WORD FIND

```
.  .  .  .  .  .  .  .  .  .  .  .  .  .  .  .  .  .
.  .  N  E  P  H  R  O  N  S  I  T  I  T  S  Y  C  .  Y  .
U  .  .  .  .  .  .  A  L  L  U  D  E  M  .  .  .  E  .
R  .  .  .  .  P  .  .  .  .  C  O  R  T  E  X  .  .  N  .
E  .  .  .  E  .  .  .  .  .  H  .  .  .  .  .  .  D  .
T  .  .  L  .  .  .  .  .  E  .  .  .  .  .  .  .  I  .
E  .  V  .  .  .  .  .  M  G  .  .  .  .  .  .  .  K  .
R  I  .  .  .  .  .  O  F  I  L  T  R  A  T  I  O  N  .
S  .  .  .  .  .  D  .  .  .  P  O  .  .  .  .  R  .  .
.  .  X  .  .  .  I  .  .  .  .  Y  .  M  .  .  .  E  .
.  .  .  Y  .  A  A  D  H  .  P  R  .  .  E  .  .  D  .
.  .  .  .  L  .  .  .  .  A  .  A  C  .  .  R  .  D  .  .
.  .  .  Y  .  A  .  P  .  .  M  .  A  .  .  U  A  .  .
.  .  S  .  .  .  C  I  .  .  .  I  .  L  .  L  .  .
.  I  .  .  .  L  .  .  .  .  D  .  .  .  C  .  B  U  .
S  .  .  .  .  L  .  .  .  .  .  S  .  .  .  .  U  .  .  S
.  .  .  .  .  A  .  .  .  .  .  .  .  .  .  .  L  .  .
.  .  .  .  .  .  .  .  .  .  .  .  .  .  .  .  .  I  .
.  .  .  .  .  E  C  N  E  N  I  T  N  O  C  N  I  .  .  .  .
.  .  .  .  M  I  C  T  U  R  I  T  I  O  N  .  .  .  .  .  .
```

CROSSWORD

```
        L
C A T H E T E R I Z A T I O N
        T               C A L Y X
        H               Y
M I C T U R I T I O N   S
  N     R               T
  C   O I       T R I G O N E
  O   L F       G     I
  N P I T G L O M E R U L U S
  T O U R       Y     I
  I L R         C
  N Y I         O
  E U           S
A N U R I A     U
  C I           R
  E A           I
                A
```

Urinary System

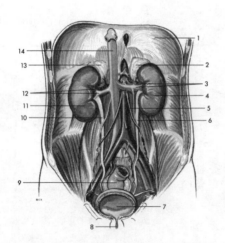

1. Diaphragm
2. Left adrenal gland
3. Left renal artery and vein
4. Left kidney
5. Aorta
6. Left ureter
7. Urinary bladder
8. Urethra
9. Rectum
10. Right ureter
11. Right kidney
12. Right renal artery and vein
13. Right adrenal gland
14. Inferior vena cava

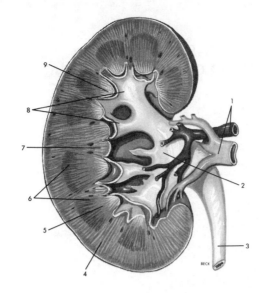

Kidney

1. Renal artery and vein
2. Pelvis
3. Ureter
4. Cortex
5. Pyramid

6. Medulla
7. Renal column
8. Calyx
9. Papilla

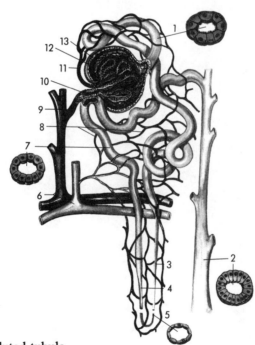

Nephron

1. Proximal convoluted tubule
2. Collecting tubule
3. Descending limb of Henle's loop
4. Ascending limb of Henle's loop
5. Segment of Henle's loop
6. Artery and vein
7. Distal convoluted tubule

8. Peritubular capillaries
9. Afferent arteriole
10. Juxtaglomerular complex
11. Efferent arteriole
12. Glomerulus
13. Bowman's capsule

CHAPTER 19
FLUID AND ELECTROLYTE BALANCE

Circle the correct response

1. Inside, p. 474
2. Extracellular, p. 474
3. Extracellular, p. 474
4. Lower, p. 474
5. More, p. 475
6. Decline, p. 474
7. Less, p. 475
8. Decreases, p. 474
9. 55%, p. 474
10. Fluid balance, p. 474

Multiple choice

11. C, p. 477
12. E, p. 477
13. A, p. 478
14. C, p. 477
15. E, p. 477
16. D, p. 477
17. D, p. 476
18. C, p. 479
19. B, p. 479
20. D, p. 479
21. E, p. 481
22. B, p. 482
23. B, p. 482
24. B, p. 482

True or false

25. Catabolism, p. 474
26. T
27. T
28. Nonelectrolyte, p. 477
29. T
30. Hypervolemia, p. 480
31. Tubular function, p. 479
32. 2400 ml, p. 477
33. T
34. 100 mEg, p. 479

Fill in the blanks

35. Dehydration, p. 482
36. Decreases, p. 482
37. Decrease, p. 482
38. Overhydration, p. 482
39. Intravenous fluids, p. 482
40. Heart, p. 482

APPLYING WHAT YOU KNOW

41. Ms. Titus could not accurately measure water intake created by foods or catabolism, nor could she measure output created by lungs, skin, or the intestines.

42. A careful record of fluid intake and output should be maintained and the patient should be monitored for signs and symptoms of electrolyte and water imbalance.

CROSSWORD

```
N O N E L E C T R O L Y T E S
  V                       L
D E H Y D R A T I O N     E
  R         N         C E
  H         I   D I U R E T I C
  Y         D O         R F
  O       I O N S   C A T I O N
  R       S S         L
  A       S           Y
  T       O           T
  I F     C           E
  O       I C F
  N       R
          T
          E
```

CHAPTER 20
ACID-BASE BALANCE

Choose the correct term

1. B, p. 486
2. A, p. 486
3. A, p. 486
4. B, p. 486
5. B, p. 486
6. B, p. 486
7. B, p. 487
8. A, p. 487
9. B, p. 487
10. B, p. 487

Multiple choice

11. E, p. 486
12. E, p. 486
13. A, p. 486
14. E, p. 490
15. C, p. 490
16. D, p. 494
17. C, p. 491
18. B, p. 491
19. D, p. 491
20. E, p. 492
21. E, p. 493

True or false

22. Buffer instead of heart, p. 486
23. Buffer pairs, p. 487
24. T
25. T
26. Alkalosis, p. 491
27. Reverse - arterial blood has a higher pH, p. 491
28. T
29. Kidneys, p. 491
30. Lungs, p. 491

Matching

31. E, p. 491
32. G, p. 494
33. F, p. 491
34. A, p. 494
35. I, p. 491

36. B, p. 494
37. H, p. 494
38. C, p. 494
39. D, p. 494
40. J, p. 491

APPLYING WHAT YOU KNOW

41. Normal saline contains chloride ions which replace bicarbonate ions and thus relieve the bicarbonate excess which occurs during severe vomiting.

42. Most citrus fruits, although acid tasting, are fully oxidized during metabolism and have little effect on acid-base balance. Cranberry juice is one of the few exceptions.

43. Milk of magnesia. It is base. Milk is slightly acidic. (see chart, p. 487)

44. WORD FIND

```
.   .   .   .   .   .   .   .   .   .   .   .   .   .   N   .
.   .  D   I   U   R   E   T   I   C   .   .   .   .   .   .  O   .
D   .   .   .   .   E   C   N   A   L   A   B   D   I   U   L   F   .   I   .
E   .   S   .   .   A   L   D   O   S   T   E   R   O   N   E   .   T   .
H   E   .   .   N   .   .   .   .   .   .   .   .   .   .   .   .   A   .
Y   L   .   .   .   O   .   .   .   .   .   .   .   .   H   R   .
D   E   .   .   .   .   I   .   .   S   .   .   .   .   .   O   .   D   .
R   C   .   .   .   .   T   O   .   .   .   K   .   M   .   .   Y   .
A   T   .   .   .   .   .   D   A   .   .   .   I   E   .   .   .   H   .
T   R   .   .   .   .   I   .   C   .   I   .   O   D   .   .   .   R   .
I   O   .   .   .   U   A   .   .   O   .   N   S   .   .   N   .   .   E   .
O   L   .   .   M   N   .   .   U   .   .   T   .   .   .   .   E   .   V   .
N   Y   .   .   I   .   .   T   .   .   A   A   .   .   .   .   D   Y   O   .
.   T   .   O   .   .   P   .   .   S   .   K   T   W   .   .   E   .   S   .
.   E   N   .   .   U   .   .   I   .   E   S   .   A   .   M   .   .   .
.   S   .   .   T   .   S   .   .   .   .   R   .   .   T   A   .   .   .
.   .   .   .   .   .   .   .   .   H   .   .   .   I   .   .   .   E   .
.   .   .   .   .   .   .   .   D   .   .   .   .   H   .   .   .   .   R   .   .
.   .   .   .   .   .   A   .   .   .   .   .   T   .   .   .   .   .   .
.   N   O   N   E   L   E   C   T   R   O   L   Y   T   E   S   .   .   .   .
```

CROSSWORD

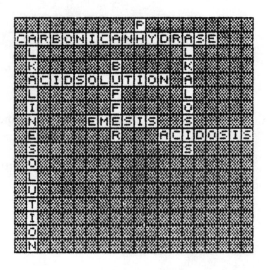

CHAPTER 21
THE REPRODUCTIVE SYSTEMS

Matching

Group A

1. D, p. 498
2. C, p. 498
3. E, p. 498
4. B, p. 499
5. A, p. 498

Group B

6. C, p. 499
7. A, p. 499
8. D, p. 498
9. B, p. 499
10. E, p. 499

Multiple choice

11. B, p. 499
12. C, p. 499
13. A, p. 500
14. D, p. 499
15. E, p. 499
16. D, p. 502
17. C, p. 503
18. C, p. 500
19. A, p. 503

Fill in the blanks

20. Testes, p. 499
21. Spermatozoa or sperm, p. 500
22. Ovum, p. 498
23. Testosterone, p. 503
24. Interstitial cells, p. 503
25. Masculinizing, p. 503
26. Anabolic, p. 503

Choose the correct term

27. B, p. 503
28. H, p. 505
29. G, p. 504
30. A, p. 503
31. F, p. 504
32. C, p. 503
33. I, p. 503
34. E, p. 504
35. D, p. 505
36. J, p. 505

Fill in the blanks

37. Oligospermia, p. 505
38. 2 months, p. 505
39. Cryptorchidism, p. 505
40. Benign prostatic hypertrophy, p. 505
41. Phimosis, p. 506
42. Impotence, p. 506
43. Hydrocele, p. 506
44. Inguinal hernia, p. 506
45. Prostate, p. 506

Matching

46. D, p. 507
47. C, p. 507
48. B, p. 507
49. A, p. 507
50. E, p. 507

Choose the correct structure

51. A, p. 512
52. B, p. 507
53. A, p. 512
54. B, p. 507
55. A, p. 512

56. A, p. 512
57. A, p. 512
58. B, p. 507

Fill in the blanks

59. Gonads, p. 507
60. Oogenesis, p. 508
61. Meiosis, p. 509
62. One half or 23, p. 509
63. Fertilization, p. 509
64. 46, p. 509
65. Estrogen, p. 509
66. Progesterone, p. 509
67. Secondary sexual characteristics, p. 509
68. Menstrual cycle, p. 509
69. Puberty, p. 509

Choose the correct structure

70. A, p. 509
71. B, p. 511
72. C, p. 511
73. B, p. 510
74. A, p. 509
75. B, p. 510
76. A, p. 510
77. A, p. 509
78. C, p. 511

Matching

Group A

79. D, p. 511
80. E, p. 511
81. B, p. 511
82. C, p. 511
83. A, p. 512

Group B

84. E, p. 512
85. A, p. 512
86. D, p. 513
87. B, p. 512
88. C, p. 513

True or false

89. Menarche, p. 513
90. One, p. 513
91. 14, p. 513
92. Menstrual period, p. 513
93. T
94. Anterior, p. 513

Choose the correct hormone

95. B, p. 513
96. A, p. 513
97. B, p. 513
98. B, p. 513
99. A, p. 513

Choose the correct response

100. F, p. 517
101. E, p. 517
102. A, p. 517
103. H, p. 516
104. I, p. 518
105. G, p. 519
106. C, p. 517
107. B, p. 516
108. L, p. 520
109. D, p. 516
110. J, p. 518
111. K, p. 520

APPLYING WHAT YOU KNOW

112. Impotent - The testes are not only essential organs of reproduction, but are also responsible for the "masculinizing" hormone. Without this hormone, Mr. Belinki will have no desire to reproduce.

113. Sterile - The sperm count may be too low to reproduce but the remaining testicle will produce enough masculinizing hormone to prevent impotency.

114. The uterine tubes are not attached to the ovaries and infections can exit at this area and enter the abdominal cavity.

115. Yes. Yes. Without the hormones from the ovaries to initiate the menstrual cycle, Mrs. Harlan will no longer have a menstrual cycle and can be considered to be in menopause. (cessation of menstrual cycle)

116. No. Ms. Comstock still will have her ovaries which are the source of her hormones. She will not experience menopause due to this procedure.

```
. . . . M . . . . . . . . . . . . . .
. . . . U . . . . . . . . . . . . . .
A . . . T . O V I D U C T S . . . . .
C . . . O . . . . . . C O W P E R S M
R . . . R . . . M . . . . . . . . . S
O . . . C . . . . E . . . . . . . . I
S S . . S . . . . . I . . . . . . . D
O N S E M I N I F E R O U S O . . . I
M E . . E N D O M E T R I U M S . . S H
E R . . . . . . . . . . . . I . I C
. E . . . . . S P E R M A T I D S M R O
. F . S . E S T R O G E N . . S . . Y O T
. E . E . . . . . . . . . P . . D I P
. D . I . . . . . . . . . . E . V I P
. S P R O S T A T E C T O M Y R . A D Y R
. A . A . . P . . . . . . . M . . G I P C
. V . V . . E . . . . . . . . . I P C
. . . O . . N . . . . . . . . N E
. . . . . . I . . . . . . . . A . .
. . . . . . S P R E G N A N C Y . . . .
```

CROSSWORD

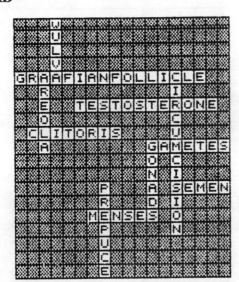

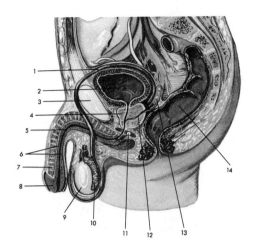

Male Reproductive Organs

1. Ductus deferens
2. Bladder
3. Symphysis pubis
4. Prostate gland
5. Urethra
6. Corpus spongiosum urethra
7. Corpus cavernosum
8. Glans penis
9. Testis
10. Epididymis
11. Bulbourethral gland
12. Ejaculatory duct
13. Seminal vesicle
14. Rectum

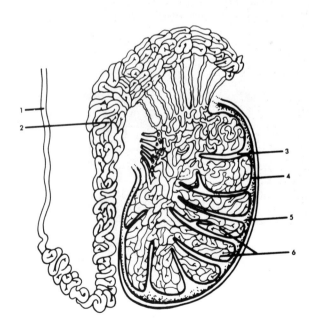

Tubules of Testis and Epididymis

1. Ductus (vas) deferens
2. Body of epididymis
3. Septum
4. Lobule
5. Tunica albuginea
6. Seminiferous tubules

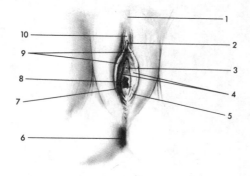

Vulva

1. Mons pubis
2. Clitoris
3. Orifice of urethra
4. Labia majora
5. Opening of greater vestibular gland
6. Anus
7. Vestibule
8. Orifice of vagina
9. Labia minora
10. Prepuce

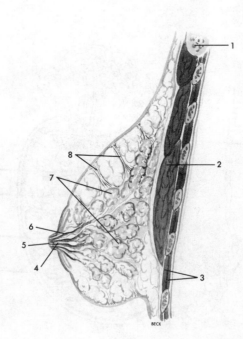

Breast

1. Clavicle
2. Pectoralis major muscle
3. Intercostal muscles
4. Duct
5. Nipple
6. Lactiferous duct
7. Alveoli
8. Suspensory ligaments of Cooper

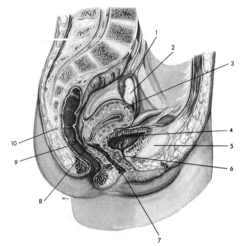

Female Pelvis

1. Fallopian tube (Uterine)
2. Ovary
3. Uterus
4. Urinary bladder
5. Symphysis pubis
6. Urethra
7. Vagina
8. Cervix
9. Rectum
10. Coccyx

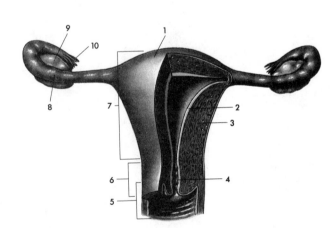

Uterus and Adjacent Structures

1. Fundus
2. Endometrium
3. Myometrium
4. Cervical canal
5. Vagina
6. Cervix
7. Body
8. Uterine (Fallopian) tube
9. Ovary
10. Fimbriae

329

CHAPTER 22
GROWTH AND DEVELOPMENT

Fill in the blanks

1. Conception, p. 528
2. Birth, p. 528
3. Embryology, p. 528
4. Oviduct, p. 528
5. Zygote, p. 528
6. Morula, p. 528
7. Blastocyst, p. 528
8. Amniotic cavity, p. 532
9. Chorion, p. 532
10. Placenta, p. 532

Choose the correct term

11. G, p. 533
12. F, p. 534
13. C, p. 539
14. B, p. 534
15. A, p. 533
16. H, p. 537
17. E, p. 537
18. D, p. 537
19. I, p. 534
20. J, p. 539

True or false

21. T
22. T
23. Placenta previa, p. 540
24. Abruptio placentae, p. 540
25. Preeclampsia, p. 540
26. Stillbirth, p. 540
27. T

Multiple choice

28. E, p. 541
29. E, p. 542
30. E, p. 542
31. A, p. 542
32. B, p. 542
33. C, p. 542
34. B, p. 542
35. D, p. 542

36. E, p. 542
37. D, p. 543
38. A, p. 543
39. C, p. 543
40. C, p. 543
41. C, p. 543
42. E, p. 543

Matching

43. F, p. 541
44. A, p. 542
45. C, p. 543
46. H, p. 543
47. D, p. 543
48. B, p. 542
49. E, p. 543
50. G, p. 542
51. I, p. 544

Fill in the blanks

52. Lipping, p. 544
53. Osteoarthritis, p. 545
54. Nephron, p. 545
55. Barrel chest, p. 545
56. Atherosclerosis, p. 545
57. Arteriosclerosis, p. 545
58. Hypertension, p. 545
59. Presbyopia, p. 545
60. Cataract, p. 546
61. Glaucoma, p. 546

Unscramble the words

62. Infancy
63. Postnatal
64. Organogenesis
65. Zygote
66. Childhood
67. Fertilization

APPLYING WHAT YOU KNOW

68. Normal
69. Only about 40% of the taste buds present at ago 30 remain at age 75
70. A significant loss of hair cells in the Organ of Corti causes a serious decline in ability to hear certain frequencies.

CROSSWORD

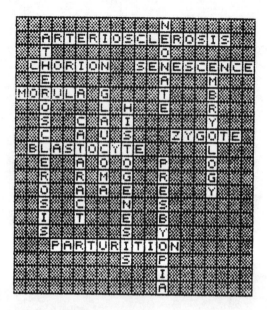

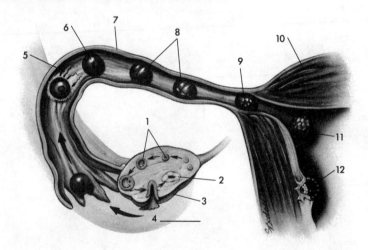

Fertilization and Implantation

1. Developing follicles
2. Corpus luteum
3. Ovary
4. Ovulation
5. Spermatozoa (Fertilization)
6. First mitosis
7. Uterine (Fallopian) tube
8. Divided zygote
9. Morula
10. Uterus
11. Blastocyst
12. Implantation

CHAPTER 23
GENETICS AND GENETIC DISEASES

Matching

1. E, p. 552
2. A, p. 552
3. B, p. 552
4. C, p. 552
5. D, p. 552

Fill in the blanks

6. Genes, p. 553
7. Dominant, p. 554
8. Recessive, p. 554
9. Carrier, p. 555
10. Co-dominance, p. 555
11. Sex, p. 555
12. Female, p. 555
13. Mutation, p. 556
14. Genetic mutation, p. 556

Matching

15. E, p. 558
16. D, p. 558
17. J, p. 558
18. F, p. 558
19. C, p. 558
20. G, p. 560
21. A, p. 558
22. H, p. 560
23. B, p. 557
24. I, p. 560

Multiple choice

25. D, p. 561
26. B, p. 561
27. C, p. 562
28. C, p. 563
29. D, p. 563
30. D, p. 564
31. B, p. 565

True or false

32. T
33. Electrophoresis, p. 564
34. Gene augmentation, p. 565
35. T
36. T

Unscramble the words

37. Carrier
38. Trisomy
39. Gene
40. Pedigree
41. Chromosome
42. Inherited

APPLYING WHAT YOU KNOW

43. In a form of dominance called co-dominance, the effect will be equal causing "light brown" to occur.

44. One in four (1 in 4) or 25%

45. Amniocentesis or chorionic villus sampling. The counselor will then produce a Karyotype to determine anomalies.

PUNNETT SQUARE

<u>Mr. Atkins PP</u>

<u>Mrs Atkins pp</u>

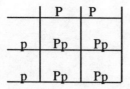

	P	P
p	Pp	Pp
p	Pp	Pp

<u>100%</u> chance of brown eyes

<u>0%</u> chance of blue eyes

Mr. Rhoades Pp

	P	p
P	PP	Pp
p	Pp	pp

a. Normal Pigmentation <u>25%</u>
b. Carriers <u>50%</u>
c. Albinism <u>25%</u>

NOTES

NOTES

NOTES

NOTES

NOTES